MW00355870

Where Young Minds Grow

ST. THOMAS SCHOOL LIBRARY

This gift was given by:
St. Thomas Staff

in memory of Beth Lee's father,

Lee Railsback

Date_____April 1995_____

ARTHUR ASHE
Against the Wind

ARTHUR ASHE
Against the Wind

by
DAVID R. COLLINS

A People in Focus Book

 **DILLON PRESS**
New York

Maxwell Macmillan Canada
Toronto

Maxwell Macmillan International
New York Oxford Singapore Sydney

Photo Credits

Photo research by Debbie Needleman

Cover courtesy of UPI/Bettmann

Back cover courtesy of AP/Wide World Photos

UPI/Bettmann: 6, 43, 67, 97; Reuters/Bettmann: 17; AP/Wide World Photos: 34, 60, 73, 81, 86, 99, 104, 108, 114, 117; Richmond Newspapers: 120-121

Book design by Carol Matsuyama

Library of Congress Cataloging-in-Publication Data

Collins, David R.

    Arthur Ashe : against the wind / by David R. Collins. — 1st ed.

       p. cm. — (People in focus)

    Includes bibliographical references and index.

    ISBN 0-382-24718-3 PBK

    ISBN 0-87518-647-5 HC

    1. Ashe, Arthur—Juvenile literature. 2. Tennis players—United States—Biography—Juvenile literature. [1. Ashe, Arthur. 2. Tennis players. 3. Afro-Americans—Biography.] I. Title. II. Title: Against the wind. III. Series: People in focus book.

GV994.A7C65   1994

796.342'092—dc20

[B]   94-17853

Copyright © 1994 by David R. Collins

All rights reserved. No part of this book may be reproduced or transmitted in any form or by any means, electronic or mechanical, including photocopying, recording, or by any information storage and retrieval system, without permission in writing from the Publisher.

Dillon Press   Maxwell Macmillan Canada, Inc.

Macmillan Publishing Company   1200 Eglinton Avenue East

866 Third Avenue   Suite 200

New York, NY 10022   Don Mills, Ontario M3C 3N1

Macmillan Publishing Company is part of the Maxwell Communication Group of Companies.

First edition

Printed in the United States of America

10 9 8 7 6 5 4 3 2 1

Contents

Introduction

He was born in a blacks-only hospital.
He grew up in blacks-only neighborhoods.
He went to blacks-only schools.

Yet Arthur Robert Ashe, Jr., rose and triumphed in a sport dominated by whites. How? Probably because he refused to let the color of his skin limit the scope of his dreams.

"Certainly I was aware that I was different," Ashe recalled. "But it never occurred to me that I couldn't reach a goal because I was a Negro. Frankly, I've never thought of myself as being a black tennis player but rather a tennis player who is black. It may sound the same, but it really isn't."

As a tennis player, Arthur Ashe, Jr., reached the heights of the sport. Ranked the top player in the world in 1975, his serve-volley was considered the best in the game. The quality of his play

Eyes glued to the ball, Arthur captures the championship at Wimbledon in 1975.

was surpassed only by his quiet, mannerly demeanor. When he disagreed with a call on the tennis court, he might flash a disappointed look at a tournament official. But that's the most irritation he would show. Good sportsmanship went with the game, just as much as a serve or a return.

Yet it was not only a racket that Arthur Ashe lifted with skill. With pen in hand, he shared his life four times on paper, his autobiographical accounts informing and inspiring, especially reaching into the hearts and minds of young people. His curiosity about black athletes in America led him to compile the three-volume *A Hard Road to Glory*, a historical account of the achievements of his race in his own country.

Beginning in 1969, Ashe waged an active war against apartheid, blasting away at the wall of prejudice against blacks in South Africa. It took four years before he could get a visa into that country, but his appearance at the tournament there opened new doors for understanding.

Ashe shared his time and talents in America, too, establishing tennis clinics in inner cities. Boys and girls, many of minority backgrounds, got their chance for instruction and competition in a sport they would never have known without Ashe's efforts.

Contracting AIDS through a transfusion of tainted blood in 1983, Ashe turned a tragedy into one more personal cause. He spoke eloquently on behalf of the disease sufferers, starting a foundation to fight the deadly illness.

On July 10, 1943, Arthur Ashe, Jr., was born in Richmond, Virginia. Only forty-nine years later, on a cold morning in February 1993, his body was carried to the governor's mansion to lie in state. Thousands passed his casket, remembering the boy who started lifting a tennis racket when it was almost bigger than he was.

A few days later, 6,500 mourners jammed the Arthur Ashe Athletic Center in Richmond to say a final farewell. His daughter, six-year-old Camera, stayed close to her mother, while national notables such as Mayor David Dinkins of New York City, Ethel Kennedy, Jesse Jackson, and U.S. Senators Bill Bradley and Charles Robb offered tributes and paid their respects.

"He took the burden of race," said Andrew Young, former U.S. delegate to the United Nations, "and wore it as a cloak of dignity."

Indeed he did. In so many ways, Arthur Ashe ran against the wind in the race of life.

Few have run the race as well.

Chapter / One

Dark Secrets

It wasn't fair. It just wasn't fair.

The tall, thin man set the telephone receiver back on the cradle. The familiar smile was gone, replaced by a deep, worried frown. During the twenty-minute conversation with *USA Today* sports editor Gene Policinski, Ashe's life had taken a tragic nosedive. His body suddenly felt much older than its forty-eight years as he faced Doug Smith, Policinski's reporter, who sat before him.

Certainly, Arthur Ashe had been in tense situations before. Usually it was a tennis match that drained him emotionally and physically. There was the U.S. Open championship of 1968, for instance. It took five long sets and every bit of stamina he could muster to outlast Tom Okker, nicknamed the "Flying Dutchman," from the Netherlands. Seven years later came the finals of the men's singles competition at Wimbledon. Defeating both the powerful Bjorn Borg and the invincible Jimmy Connors to cop the coveted Wimbledon Cup was not easy, either. There were the Davis Cup matches and many more. In each case, Ashe became more than a winner. He was a "first" in the sports history books. No black tennis player had ever reached the heights that he had climbed, and none of his achievements had come easily.

It was not merely the sports competition that had taken its toll on Arthur Ashe. Sometimes it was the obstacle course that went with it, the personal drain and strain. In 1969, he was banned from playing in the South African Open. It seemed impossible that one of the top players in the world would not be allowed to compete because of the color of his skin. But it had happened. And the experience opened a longtime personal battle against apartheid for Ashe.

Then there was that ugly libel suit concerning the Davis Cup team—once more the opponent was Jimmy Connors. And there was the campaign to promote players' rights. There were the protests, too, on behalf of humane causes, that took the quiet, laid-back gentleman to jail on more than one occasion.

But most recently, it was the medical roller coaster that had pulled Ashe in every direction. In 1979, when he was only thirty-six years old, a heart attack led to quadruple bypass surgery. Since then the tennis great and political activist had fought off health problems. In 1983, he needed a double bypass operation. One of these operations, probably the second, had led to the present dilemma. Arthur Ashe was now confronting the greatest challenge of his life. So often he had battled the injustice of racial prejudice. Now he faced the hardships of having AIDS and of letting the world know.

For almost four long years, Ashe had carried the dark secret. In 1988, before he underwent brain surgery, hospital studies revealed that he had tested positive for HIV, the virus that causes AIDS. After further investigation, doctors believed that he had probably become infected as a result of his 1983 operation. He had received two units of blood at that time, twenty-two months before tests for HIV became routine.

Arthur and his wife, Jeanne, wrestled with the decision in 1988 of whether to go public with the news of the infection. Ultimately, they decided to keep the matter quiet. After all, Ashe reasoned, he was not running for public office, which would make it necessary to reveal the state of his health. And he did not have stockholders to report to as a company executive. At best, he fell under the "dubious umbrella of a public figure." To Arthur and Jeanne, that hardly required revealing the condition of his health. An announcement that he was HIV positive would have permanently and unnecessarily infringed upon his family's right to privacy. Of paramount importance to the couple was the well-being of their one-year-old daughter, Camera.

But now the shade was drawn, the curtain was lifted. Someone had "ratted" on him by calling *USA Today* and tipping the newspaper off about Ashe's condition. Now Arthur sat with Doug Smith, the sports reporter sent by Gene Policinski. Years before, Ashe and Smith had played tennis together as boys in Richmond, Virginia. But today Smith had not come to reminisce about the good old days. "Give Smith the story," Policinski had said on the telephone. Rumors had circulated that Ashe was HIV positive. Was it true?

Of course, it would not be the first time a major black athlete had admitted to having the AIDS virus. In November 1991 Earvin "Magic" Johnson, the basketball megastar, had announced that he was HIV positive. But in Arthur's mind, Johnson's case was different. Magic was an active athlete at the time, in the middle of a magnificent career with the Los Angeles Lakers. Magic had little choice but to reveal his medical condition. To suddenly leave the team with no explanation was impossible. But Ashe was not in the spotlight like Magic Johnson. Who had tipped off the newspaper about his condition? Why couldn't the newspaper just ignore the story? It was Smith's appearance and persistent questioning that led Ashe to call Policinski. The twenty-minute call had changed Ashe's life.

"Could be." That was the answer Ashe gave to Policinski when asked if he had the dreaded virus. How easy it would have been to lie, to try to put the newspaper editor off. But lies did not come easily to Arthur Ashe. Instead, he asked Policinski for thirty-six hours before publishing anything. Ashe wanted to make some calls and arrange some sort of public announcement. Policinski did not like the idea of being told when news stories should be published. Yet this story had an unusual twist to it. The tip about Ashe's illness had come into the USA *Today* offices anonymously, and the paper had a policy of not publishing reports from unnamed sources without independent confirmation. "Could be" was hardly independent confirmation.

Arthur decided to share the news himself. In

the hours that followed that telephone conversation, Ashe huddled closely with his wife. Jeanne
Ashe was actually somewhat relieved that he was
finally going public with the secret they had kept
for nearly four years. Keeping that secret had not
been easy. Only their closest friends and a small circle of New York doctors knew. Now that circle
expanded, as Ashe alerted other friends and family
members he felt should know before he announced
his condition to the world.

On Wednesday, April 8, 1992, Arthur Ashe
faced reporters in the Home Box Office headquar-
ters in New York City. Ashe was a regular HBO
commentator during the Wimbledon tennis matches. Jeanne stood nearby, as did New York's mayor
David N. Dinkins, a personal friend and occasional
tennis partner. Ashe made no attempt to hide his
anger about being placed in this situation by an
anonymous informer and *USA Today*.

"Somebody just called up the newspaper and
ratted on me," said Ashe, "and so they felt journal-
istically they had to follow up, and I was the victim.
I just didn't want to go public now because I am not
sick."

Carefully, Ashe laid out the history of his AIDS
condition as he saw it, emphasizing his appreciation
of the "silent and generous conspiracy" among the

medical community to keep his illness secret. "We are 100 percent sure the cause of my HIV infection was a blood transfusion either after my 1979 bypass operation or the '83 operation," Ashe declared at the press conference. "We are 95 percent sure it was the '83 operation."

As to his present condition? "I can still play thirty-six holes of golf without a golf cart," Ashe boasted to reporters. "I have good days and I have bad days. My ratio of good days to bad days is about six to one. I don't think anybody in my stage of this would be able to go through with no bad days."

His anger provided Ashe with a certain degree of strength and dignity as he read his prepared statement. But he lost his composure when he reached a poignant paragraph about his daughter. As tears flooded his eyes, he turned to Jeanne for help. She continued his statement: "Even though we've begun preparing Camera for this news, beginning tonight, Jeanne and I must teach her how to react to new, different, and sometimes cruel comments that have little to do with her reality." A relieved Arthur Ashe announced that both Jeanne and Camera had tested negative for HIV.

Despite the number of people present, the hotel room occasionally fell silent. The only sounds heard were camera shutters clicking. In addition

Jeanne looks on as her husband makes his startling announcement that he is HIV positive.

to the 150 newspaper and magazine reporters present, 30 TV camera operators were there to film the conference.

And then it was over. Quickly the hotel room emptied as journalists hurried back to their desks, their telephones, and their studios. Certainly, Arthur was the newsmaker of the day.

Gene Policinski was immediately put on the defensive. Many agreed with Ashe that the newspaper had indeed invaded his privacy. Policinski stood firm, claiming that the health problems of public figures was news: "Mr. Ashe's life affects a great many people. So there is no question in my mind that it legitimately is news, and I think we went about it in a responsible fashion."

Arthur Ashe would have argued the point, but he now had other matters on his mind. How to tell little Camera was the first consideration. Before that time came, however, he spoke with President George Bush on the telephone. The chief executive offered his prayers and concern. Perhaps Ashe might want to assist the National Commission on AIDS? Perhaps. There would be time to consider that later.

Or would there? Time. Suddenly the awareness of time occupied Arthur's thoughts. As outer appearances go, time had been good to him. The 155 pounds he carried still stretched evenly over his 6-foot 1-inch frame, and his face remained unlined and lean. Aviator glasses not only corrected Ashe's vision but contributed to a boyish and scholarly look. His hair was full and minus even a hint of gray.

Yet his body had grown accustomed to regular medication. In addition to five pills each day for heart disease, he took AZT, a medicine believed to slow the progress of HIV, three times a day; an antibiotic four times a day; and an antifungus drug to prevent a condition called thrush (whitening of the inside of the mouth). Every month he underwent treatment to prevent him from contracting pneumonia. Despite his medical agenda, though, the former tennis great never thought of himself as a sick man.

With his public announcement concerning the AIDS virus, Arthur Ashe suddenly looked at time with a new awareness. He had an eerie sense of its passage as he read the newspaper accounts in the days following the press conference. Many stories traced his entire life, reaching back to its beginning.

The date was July 10, 1943. As the bombs of World War II exploded far away, loud squeals were coming from a young baby boy in the delivery room of St. Phillip's Hospital, a medical center for blacks, in Richmond. Already, Arthur Robert Ashe, Jr., was "raising a racket."

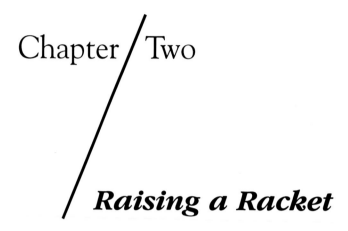

Chapter / Two

Raising a Racket

The new son of Arthur Ashe, Sr., and his wife, Mattie, was a healthy baby, blessed with a hearty set of lungs and a cry that kept nurses running to his cribside.

From St. Phillip's Hospital, Arthur was taken home. Home was his uncle's house in Richmond. It wasn't that his parents were unable to afford a place of their own. Rather, the Ashe family was a close unit that liked to stay together. Arthur Ashe, Sr., often juggled two or three jobs at a time, serving as a gardener, carpenter, and chauffeur—typical positions for a black man in the South during the 1940s. Not every employment door was open to blacks. Although World War II had taken many men into military service, some employers simply cut their payrolls or hired women.

There were uglier reasons, too, for the shortage of jobs for African Americans. "I'd rather do without somethin' before I'd hire a black man," more than one businessman declared. "Never knew a black man worth hiring."

Those businessmen had never met Arthur Ashe, Sr. Determined to provide a good life for his family, he often worked fourteen hours a day. When Arthur, Jr., was four, the Ashe family relocated to a five-room frame house on Sledd Street. The building sat alone in the middle of a blacks-only park area. The Ashe home was one of the benefits provided to the elder Ashe in return for his services as a special police officer. He supervised Richmond's biggest playground, Brook Field Park, which stretched over eighteen acres.

To many families, living in a house without any close neighbors would hardly be an ideal situation. But Arthur Ashe, Sr., always found the good side of whatever happened. As a gardener, he loved raising the healthiest flowers, even if they belonged to someone else. As a chauffeur, it did not bother him that he was driving another person's car. As a carpenter, he took pride in the shelves he put together, in the tables and chairs he could make. "Mr. Ashe was a giving man," observed Westcott Turner, a family friend, who benefited from Ashe's flower-growing skills. "He was glad he had the talents to make people happy, to make their lives better."

But for all the work he did for his employers, there was never a doubt that his family came first in his life. His wife, Mattie Cordell Cunningham Ashe, whom he lovingly called "Baby," and his son, Arthur, received every bit of attention he could provide.

People got used to seeing the Ashe family on the swings and slides at Brook Field's playgrounds. As for young Arthur, it was fun having his own out-door toys. "Come push me," he learned to say early, while standing near the baby swing. "Ple-ease." If there was one thing his father insisted upon, it was good manners.

Soon Arthur, Jr., explored beyond the nearby swings and slides. Brook Field Park boasted an entire complex. Richmond residents swarmed to enjoy the baseball diamonds and basketball courts, as well as the Olympic-sized swimming pool.

But for young Arthur, the four hard-surfaced tennis courts were the star attraction. Not only could he hit a ball back and forth with friends; there was also a backboard to hit against when he was alone. His arms and legs might be, as he admit-ted later, as "thin as soda straws," but the six-year-old could swing a tennis racket fast and hard. His responses came instinctively, his legs springing for-ward, then back like some kind of wary cat. When other kids grew tired and begged off, Arthur coaxed them to hit the ball "just a minute or two more."

In 1948, young Arthur welcomed a brother into the family. Baby John seemed to be a quieter infant than Arthur, but the new addition was "a crawler." Arthur felt himself quite important when told to "keep an eye on John," and the older boy yelled to his parents whenever the baby even looked as if he might leave his crib and playpen.

By the time Arthur walked into his first grade classroom at Baker Street Elementary School, he was a quick and able reader. Mattie Ashe could take credit for that. The Ashe family traveled little because of Arthur, Sr.,'s job, but his son discovered that the pages of magazines and books were tickets to anywhere. Give the boy a copy of *National Geographic* and he was quiet the entire afternoon. Different peoples and places fascinated him. He tested his family and friends with endless questions about African tribes or the Ice Age, life in London or the dinosaur era. Teachers commented on his quick and eager mind and rewarded his classroom contributions with top grades.

After school, Arthur became his father's helper. He raced home to do his chores in Brook

Field Park. The boy swept and raked picnic areas and chopped wood for burning. He greeted visitors with a smile and offered to help them. Yet whenever he could, Arthur found time to hit the tennis ball.

By March 1950, Mattie Ashe was pregnant with her third child. Young Arthur and John looked forward to having another brother or a sister. Minor surgery was scheduled before she was due. "Nothing to worry about," their father said, and Arthur, Jr., remembered his mother in a blue corduroy robe, standing in the doorway while he ate his breakfast.

It was the last time the boy saw his mother. After Mattie's operation, her health worsened. Toxemia, a poisonous condition of the blood, set in. A few days later, she was dead. It was a devastated Arthur Ashe, Sr., who held his two sons close and cried, "This is all I got left."

Six-year-old Arthur did not attend his mother's funeral. He couldn't bring himself to go. Bewildered and grieving, the young boy said his own private farewell as she lay in her casket in the living room. Family and friends then gathered at the Westwood Baptist Church for final services, while Arthur watched from a neighbor's window.

The Ashe house became a quieter place. Knowing that he couldn't handle two sons on his own, their father hired an elderly widow to help care for the family. Mrs. Otis Berry was loving and kind. The Ashe boys tested her strength and endurance. If there was an illness to be caught, it seemed young Arthur and John caught it. Whether it was measles or whooping cough, mumps or chicken pox, Arthur and John grabbed the sickness and held it for dear life. A bout with diphtheria was especially difficult, but slowly both boys recovered. Although tiny and skinny, Arthur moved with poise and speed. At school, he proved an able baseball player. At home, though, it was tennis that captured his attention.

Slowly, Arthur's world expanded. He was drawn to the sixteen tennis courts at Byrd Park, a whites-only tennis complex, where the boy could watch but not play. No doubt he would have loved to run onto the courts, waving his racket and challenging anyone willing to take him on. Instead, he stood behind the fence until someone shouted at him to go back to his "own part of town."

The Brook Field courts were Arthur's domain. He was familiar with every bump and crack in the hard-cover surfaces. It did not take him long to get to know Ronald Charity, a college student who was the best black tennis player in Richmond and who came to Brook Field Park to teach tennis during the summers. Charity whizzed around the courts; he pounded in quick, sure serves and placed shots with a sharp eye. Most seven-year-olds might be happy to swat a ball back and forth over the net. Not Arthur Ashe. He longed to move and hit like Ronald Charity. When Charity offered to help Arthur, the boy could not believe his ears. Charity was a tough teacher, demanding dedication and discipline. "You start with the right grip," declared Charity. "If you aren't holding the racket correctly, you might as well forget the rest of your game." Forehand, backhand, service—hour after hour the two practiced. They played games, moved on to sets, and finally played matches that lasted all afternoon.

At age eight, Arthur entered his first competition. He battered the ball, pounded the ball, banged the ball—and lost the tournament. He consoled himself with the fact that his opponent was eleven—but still, the taste of defeat was unpleasant. "I wasn't so unhappy that I wanted to quit or anything. I liked the taste of competition," Arthur remembered. "I knew, however, that I didn't like losing at all."

With the help of Ron Charity, Ashe entered many all-black tournaments in Richmond. The boy started winning, and it felt good. His strokes grew stronger, his placement of shots more accurate. Soon he was looking over his shoulder, hoping that someone might be watching and admiring his increasing skill. Arthur's posing did not impress Charity, who told the boy to knock off his "grandstanding" or he would quit working with him. Arthur complied. He knew how much Charity had helped him, and the young tennis player wanted all the help he could get.

More help arrived in the form of Dr. Robert Walter Johnson, a well-known black physician who had discovered his own love for tennis when he was in his thirties. He had a private court at his luxury home in Lynchburg, about 95 miles west of Richmond. After he no longer competed in tournaments himself, Johnson turned his attention to coaching young blacks who showed talent. His son, Bobby, also helped. At Charity's request, Dr. Johnson attended a tennis match at Virginia Union University and watched ten-year-old Arthur Ashe. The retired physician was impressed. Before long, the boy was part of Johnson's vigorous summer program at his home, which offered promising young players both instruction and competition.

"Throw that ball a bit higher when you serve."

"Bend those legs when you return that backhand."

"Don't swat the ball. Stroke it. Stroke it."

Johnson's voice pounded into Ashe. Sometimes the doctor's advice conflicted with Charity's.
Arthur loyally and stubbornly stuck by his first
teacher's lessons until his father had to jump into
his car and travel to Lynchburg. "Mr. Charity fixed
it for you to come here," the elder Ashe asserted.
"Now Dr. Johnson's your teacher. You listen to him.
If you don't want to obey him, come home." There
was no mistaking that tone in his father's voice. In
an intense two-week session during the summer,
the boy played, ate, thought, and slept tennis.
Rules. Hints. Directions. Scoldings. It was all part
of the program.

Johnson's Junior Development Team traveled
from tournament to tournament. There were six
players on the team. When they weren't practicing
or competing on the court, they helped tend
Johnson's house and grounds. The doctor's dogs
needed feeding and walking, the lawn and three-
story house required upkeep, and, of course, the
tennis court had to be in top condition at all times.
Arthur's former work at Brook Field Park came in
handy now. He could complete his chores in half
the time the others needed.

Every morning Ashe was the first one on the
court. While the others stole a few extra winks,

Arthur banged the ball against the backboard. Sometimes his campmates complained about the noise, but the additional workout time paid off. The "soda straw" arms and legs filled out, and Arthur moved around the court with precision, speed, and grace.

Johnson's program emphasized practice and drill. Forehand approach shots, forehand passing shots, forehand across-the-court shots—100 of each. Then the same for the backhand. "Another time. Take it again." Johnson's voice resounded through the hot, muggy air. High lob shots, low lob shots, smash shots. "Try it again." The Ball-Boy machine whizzed the spheres to waiting rackets. "Lower your grip." Muscles strained. Run to the net. Smash. "Double fault." Sweat soaked through shirts and shorts. "Out!" The call was close. "Don't waste energy getting angry. Put it into your game." Hour after hour. Day after day. Practice and drill. Drill and practice.

"You've got to maximize your strengths and minimize your weaknesses," Johnson declared. Young Ashe listened closely. No matter how hard he tried, his serve was not the bullet ball that others shot across the net. He knew he had to be accurate. Opponents might well have more force and power, so shot placement was especially important.

Endurance was important, too. "Sometimes you can beat a better player by just wearing him out," said Johnson. "The main idea is to get the ball back. It doesn't have to be going 100 miles an hour. It just has to be in the opponent's court."

And as if the court routine wasn't enough, Arthur surrounded himself with tennis books and magazines. He read of Tony Trabert, Jack Kramer—and, of course, the invincible Pancho Gonzales. As a Hispanic growing up in Los Angeles, Gonzales had taken his share of abuse from the young white players on the California courts. Ashe identified with Gonzales and dreamed of someday playing him.

Johnson's Junior Development Team headed to tournaments near Lynchburg and beyond. Sometimes they traveled as far as Baltimore, Maryland, or Washington, D.C. Johnson demanded quality behavior both on and off the court. "There can be a good excuse for a missed shot," said the retired physician. "There is no excuse for poor manners."

For eight consecutive summers, Ashe headed to Dr. Johnson's summer tennis camp. As the boy neared his teens, a growth spurt sent him climbing to 6 feet. His size helped his game; now he could race from line to line as well as extend his racket to snag balls his opponents thought were winners. In

1955, Ashe captured the singles championship in the American Tennis Association's twelve-and-under competition, then teamed up with Willis Thomas to win the ATA doubles tournament.

The American Tennis Association boasted the finest black tennis players in the country. But Arthur Ashe wanted to enter more white tournaments. Johnson sent the boy's entry papers to a Richmond match sponsored by the Middle Atlantic chapter of the U.S. Lawn Tennis Association (USLTA). His application was turned down because he was black.

The rejection was a bitter blow. Arthur was tired of doors being shut in his face because of his color. There were restaurants for whites and restaurants for blacks, the same as with schools and parks. Black people stood up on buses if white people wanted to sit down. In theaters that blacks were allowed to attend with whites, the blacks sat high in the balcony. "The crow's nest," the section was called. Even public bathrooms displayed WHITES ONLY signs. Prejudice was a way of life in the nation, and few blacks challenged the system. It would be hopeless. Young Arthur Ashe went along with the system just as his father had. But the boy didn't like it.

Bigotry wasn't the only problem Arthur

encountered. Trouble sometimes came from his black classmates. He worked hard in school, and his grades showed it. But not all his classmates respected his efforts. "Teacher's pet," some jeered. Others shoved him around and ripped his clothes. "Better get home, Arthur, or your daddy will whip your butt."

The hazing hurt Arthur. But he wasn't going to stop striving for good grades. Good grades meant a better job someday. As for his father, so what if he was strict and wanted the boy home right after school? It was better than having a dad who didn't care at all.

Sometimes the teasing about tennis really made Arthur angry, though. "Tennis is for sissies," some guys would say. They didn't know how demanding the sport could be. "It takes every bit of mental and physical power you can pull from your-self," Pancho Gonzales declared in magazine arti-cles, "in order to be a good tennis player. Those who say differently do not understand the game." But for a time, Arthur focused on baseball, winning a varsity spot on the Maggie Walker High School squad when he was a sophomore. No one called baseball players sissies. It was good to get away from the hazing. Thanks to his tennis workouts, Arthur had developed a good strong right arm, just what a pitcher needed.

But Walker High's principal, J. Harry Williams, summoned Arthur to his office after the boy's first game. Williams thought it foolish for Ashe to play baseball when he was making such a name for himself in tennis. Year after year he had won the ATA championship. Might pitching damage his arm? Reluctantly, Ashe agreed to set baseball aside for tennis.

Williams's advice seemed right on target. By 1958, the U.S. Lawn Tennis Association ranked Arthur as the fifth top tennis player in the country under the age of fifteen. He continued to win tournaments. As he completed his junior year in high school, he was on many people's minds.

One of them was Richard Hudlin of St. Louis, Missouri. The high school history teacher was a longtime tennis advocate. A player for some fifty years, he was now interested in helping future champions. Hudlin visited Harry Burrus, the athletic director at Washington University in St. Louis. "You ought to help a player from Richmond I've heard something about," Burrus told his friend. "Young Arthur Ashe."

"If he's as good as you say he is, I want to help him all I can," Hudlin agreed.

Before long, the phone wires jangled between

Sixteen-year-old Arthur (far right) shakes hands before competing in a tournament at Forest Hills, New York.

St. Louis and Richmond. Then the line reached to Lynchburg and Dr. Johnson. Discussion focused on the possibility that Arthur could come to St. Louis for a year.

"What about expenses?"

"Mr. Hudlin will take care of them."

Ron Charity got involved, too. Conversations were long. At first, Arthur's father opposed the whole idea. For five years he had been a widower. But now he was remarried, and Lorene Kimbrough Ashe was just finding her place in the family. Was it wise to send Arthur away for a whole year?

"He needs to play tennis all year long if he plans to play professionally someday," said Dr. Johnson. "St. Louis offers a great situation."

"He won't get any better in Richmond," added Ron Charity. "There's no real competition for him around here."

Gradually, Arthur Ashe, Sr., recognized the advantages of letting his son go to St. Louis. But he decided to let the boy make the final decision.

Arthur struggled to make up his mind. He knew he had peaked in his present surroundings. He wasn't even required to attend tennis practice as part of the high school team anymore. He merely showed up for the matches—and won. St. Louis offered many new opportunities, such as playing on indoor courts during the winter. Richmond's indoor courts were restricted to the whites during the winter.

"There's no color line in sports around here," Richard Hudlin promised. That thought was refreshing to Arthur. But leaving Richmond meant leaving family and friends, a particularly hard move just before his senior year of high school. The decision caused the young man many sleepless nights.

Chapter / Three

"Go West, Young Man"

September 1960.

The bus hissed like a giant snake as it pulled to a halt in the St. Louis terminal. Seventeen-year-old Arthur Ashe stuffed a magazine into his duffel bag, slipped down the aisle, and exited. He hoped he had made the right decision. Richmond lay far away. He knew he would miss the family and friends who had offered him so much love and support. Here he was, a stranger in a new world. But if his father, Ron Charity, and Dr. Johnson all thought this was the right thing to do, who was he to argue?

In moments Arthur felt himself swept up by Richard Hudlin and his wife, Jane. It was clear they had been looking forward to their visitor's arrival. Arthur, shy and quiet around strangers, did little more than nod as the Hudlins drove to their home.

But when Richard Hudlin laid down the house rules for Arthur, the boy spoke up. He protested having to be in bed every night, including Fridays and Saturdays, by eleven o'clock. After all, he *was* a senior in high school now.

Hudlin simply shook his head, his jaws locked. The rules stood as given. No exceptions. As far as he was concerned, Arthur had come to St. Louis to play tennis. It would be nice if he also kept up his grades. Arthur's transcript from Maggie Walker High in Richmond showed that he had an A average through his junior year. But perhaps the schoolwork in St. Louis was more difficult. Would he be able to get the same top grades at Sumner High? Only time and Arthur himself would determine that. As for Richard Hudlin, he would provide everything he could to see that Arthur succeeded. In particular, Hudlin made sure that Arthur had proper nourishment (Jane Hudlin's knowledge as a nurse would help), clean and wholesome living conditions (the Hudlins' home was no mansion, but it was spacious and comfortable and Arthur had his own room), and plenty of sleep. Arthur's pleas for more free time fell on deaf ears. "Take it or leave it!" was Hudlin's dictate. Under the circumstances, Arthur had to take it.

Arthur took something else in November 1960.

He entered the U.S. Lawn Tennis Association's
Junior Indoor singles tournament. Having little
experience on indoor courts, Arthur felt his
chances of winning were slim. Dr. Johnson had
talked about the tournament often, always wishing
that a black might capture the coveted title. He
had even entered several of the Junior
Development Team members from time to time.
But no luck. Someone else always captured the
title. This time, Arthur made it to the final round,
going up against top-seeded Frank Froehling. Two
years older than Ashe, Froehling was clearly the
favorite.

But Arthur was determined to win. He used his
usual never-give-up-a-shot attitude to combat
Froehling's pound-and-pulverize style. In a grueling
four-and-a-half-hour championship match of five
sets, 6-1, 16-14, 9-11, 3-6, 6-1, Ashe emerged the
victor. It was the biggest thrill of his life. Excited
and happy, he called Dr. Johnson to share the news.

As time passed, Hudlin's drill-sergeant
demeanor mellowed a bit. Arthur's routine reas-
sured the tough tutor. After school each day,
Arthur headed to Washington University's outdoor
courts for several hours of practice. Then it was
home to study. No "blow-off" courses for Arthur,
either. He was college-bound, without a doubt, and

his academic load demanded term papers and tests. Richard Hudlin was impressed with his boarder's work ethic, his dedication to both tennis and schooling. The eleven o'clock rule bent a bit on Arthur's behalf.

Slowly the boy came out of his shell. Or rather, his classmates helped pull him out. After all, here was a kid who had come all the way from Richmond, Virginia, to play tennis at Sumner. He was no ordinary jock. He was ranked in the nation! "Was it tenth?" one classmate would ask. "I heard third," another would answer. Whatever the case, he was a star athlete, being groomed for professional status. Besides that, the guy scored top grades in every class he took. Some kids headed over to Washington University to watch him play tennis after school. Arthur liked the special attention. He started dating, too, finding himself highly sought after by girls who seemed awed by his intelligence and sports talent. Letters home to Richmond showed Arthur gaining confidence in himself and happy with his decision to come to St. Louis. "I am always busy," he wrote, "but it's a good busy. I feel I'm spending my time right, because there isn't a minute to waste."

When weather pulled Arthur indoors for tennis workouts, he played at the 138th Infantry

Armory. On slick wooden boards, Arthur's game changed. In the past, he had relied on outlasting his opponents, a back-and-forth kind of match with Arthur hanging close to the baseline. But now he became faster on his feet, picking up the ball early after the bounce, returning it, then dashing to the net. The pro at the armory, Larry Miller, showed Arthur how to put some power into his serve and shorten his backswing.

In December, Arthur headed to Miami Beach, Florida, to compete in the Orange Bowl Juniors singles tournament. The trip offered a bonus thrill—a chance to swing up to Richmond and spend a day with his family over the Christmas vacation.

It was a noisy reunion. Everyone talked at once, most wanting to know all about Arthur. As for him, he could not get over his brother, Johnny. Although five years younger, he stood two inches taller than Arthur. The boy had splashed his way to countless swimming medals and also excelled at baseball, basketball, and football. He had even "lettered" in tennis. Johnny grabbed his brother and wrestled him to the floor just as in years past.

The family had just finished dinner that night when the telephone rang. It was for Arthur. J. D. Morgan, the athletic director and tennis coach at the University of California at Los Angeles, was on the other end.

"How'd you like to come to UCLA," Morgan asked, "with our help in paying your way—and play tennis for us?"

Arthur gulped.

Little did Arthur know that Morgan had scouted him when he played in a tournament two years earlier. The UCLA coach had contacted Dr. Johnson at that time and kept in contact since, carefully charting Arthur's tennis progress. It was just like Dr. Johnson to keep the whole thing a secret! Now that Arthur was ready to pick a college, Morgan hoped he would consider UCLA. It was the first time UCLA would be offering a scholarship to a black tennis player.

It did not take Arthur long to make up his mind. UCLA was among the top tennis schools in the nation—perhaps *the* top school. Not only that, its academic program was terrific, too. Anybody would jump at such an opportunity.

"Don't worry," Arthur told Coach Morgan. "I'll be there!"

As the thrilled high school senior hung up the phone, the magic of the moment remained. What a Christmas present! What a great Christmas present!

Chapter / Four

Discoveries

It was a proud Arthur Ashe who accepted his diploma from Sumner High School in June 1961. He did so with the highest grade point average in his class. The strains of "Pomp and Circumstance" provided a victory march for the transfer student as he strode into the graduation exercises.

In Richmond that summer, it was not easy to stay focused on tennis—Arthur could hardly wait to enter UCLA. Yet he managed to snag the USLTA National Interscholastic singles championship and to reach the semifinals of both the National Jaycees and National Juniors tournaments. He also won a berth on the Junior Davis Cup team. Sometimes he fantasized about being on the real Davis Cup team, representing his country against other nations.

Summer of '61: Arthur takes the title with ease at the National Interscholastic singles competition.

Despite his summer tennis triumphs and his eagerness to go to UCLA, Ashe felt sad at saying good-bye to his family in the fall. After all, Richmond and Los Angeles were at opposite ends of the country. Also, he'd always had someone keeping an eye on him, making sure he got enough rest and proper nourishment, checking on his grades, taking care of his laundry. All that would change now. His life would be in his own hands; he would be making his own decisions. The prospect sounded wonderful and exciting. At the same time, it seemed frightening and lonely.

"It seemed best to concentrate on the two reasons I was at UCLA," Ashe recalled later. "I wanted a good education and I wanted to play the best tennis of my life. Actually, the reasons were probably reversed at the time. I wanted to play great tennis and get a good education."

Ashe slid smoothly into the classroom routine at UCLA. In high school, both at Maggie Walker and at Sumner, he was the pacesetter. His grades always rested at the top of the curve. Getting a B troubled the young scholar. But UCLA was different, as Arthur quickly learned. Other students topped him academically. It took a while to adjust to being less than number one. Once he did, Arthur began balancing a life between studies and social activities. A friend's question "Want to get a pizza?" got a quick "Sure, why not?" from the young man from Richmond. Dances and movies attracted him, too, sometimes with a date and other times with the guys.

Still, Arthur's world at UCLA revolved around the tennis courts. Coach Morgan saw to that. "You can't just play tennis if you really want to be good at this game. You have to live it—thinking, breathing, feeling the game every minute of your life. Then, with luck, you might actually do something worthwhile with this sport."

Much of Morgan's coaching technique emphasized the mental side of tennis. Most of the players entering UCLA displayed physical strengths of one sort or another on the court. Some possessed a strong serve, others a super forehand, while a few showed a quick, agile backhand. There were those who loved the net action and others who enjoyed the solid stroking from the baseline. Coach Morgan knew how to put the polish on any player's game. But without the proper attitude, a tennis player would never be a champion.

Arthur brought the right raw materials to UCLA. Physically, he was slight, only 155 pounds attached to a 6-foot 1-inch frame. Yet the flesh that shaped his build was muscle—clean, tough muscle.

His slim, taut form moved smoothly, forward, backward, to the side. He banged a pretty good serve, too. It was the mental attitude that needed nourishment.

"I had been the best for quite some time," Arthur recalled. "At UCLA there were better players than I was. Sure, I knew what I had to do with my game, but it was more than trying harder. I had to perfect every skill I had. That demanded more than what I could physically do with my body. Tennis demands total concentration and focus. Without that, you might as well pack up your racket and get off the court."

Total focus and concentration on the game— Coach Morgan pounded that philosophy into his players:

> • If there's an explosion in the stands while you're playing, you won't hear it. Your mind is riveted to the match.

> • You're not just playing an opponent, you're playing yourself. There's no joy in winning if it means just beating the player on the other side of the net.

> • You have to leave the court knowing you

have done your best, played to your maximum ability. Then, and only then, can you feel satisfied with your performance.

Up to this time, Arthur had always played for his father, for Dr. Johnson, or for Richard Hudlin. But now his responsibility was to himself. And Arthur liked the feeling of being independent. If he could do well at UCLA, there was no telling where his game of tennis might lead.

As a freshman on the UCLA team, Arthur filled the number three slot, behind Charles Pasarell and Dave Reed. Pasarell was the reigning National Juniors champion, while Reed held the Southern California Juniors title. "These are quality guys," Arthur wrote home, "both on and off the court." Before long, Ashe and Pasarell were rooming together.

Choosing a major proved a challenge to Arthur. For a while he flip-flopped between engineering and architecture. Coach Morgan suggested business administration. "You've got a tight schedule, Arthur. Don't go too hard on yourself."

Business administration proved to be a wise suggestion. It wasn't just the classes and tennis that demanded Arthur's time; every male freshman and sophomore was required to take ROTC (Reserve

Officers' Training Corps). After the two-year requirement was completed, a student could continue or drop out. Arthur assumed he'd be drafted after college. By taking ROTC for four years, he was assured of an officer's position in the army after graduation.

Also, Arthur's scholarship at UCLA had a few strings attached. It required him to work on campus 250 hours a year. His job of keeping the tennis courts and surrounding area in tip-top shape reminded Arthur of the Brook Field Park days back in Richmond. He missed his father's stern voice giving orders, telling him to "Get a move on, boy!" But the constant sun offered a welcome change from dark and drearier days back east. California's climate allowed tennis action all year long.

Arthur faced another adjustment—losing. At Maggie Walker High and at Sumner High, the victories had come easily. Not at UCLA. On the big-college tennis circuit, Arthur found himself humbled again and again. Competition was tough. If losing wasn't bad enough, Coach Morgan usually shared a few comments, too. The only thing hotter than a blazing sun was a steaming J. D. Morgan, especially if he felt that players weren't giving their best.

Arthur had few problems with the physical end

of the game. His shots were fast and carefully placed. With each match, his serve seemed to improve. It was almost impossible to put a ball past him at the net. But his ability to concentrate proved a constant challenge.

"I can't always keep my mind firmly fixed on the game," Arthur admitted.

Coach Morgan shook his head. "If you can't do that, hang up your racket."

Arthur was not about to hang up anything. He struggled all the harder to keep his attention focused on the game. He knew the difference between hitting a volley and an overhead. Serving and stroking a forehand required two different physiological functions, too. Practice and memory, however, could smooth out those skills. Focus. Get the mind fixed. No daydreaming allowed. The next point was all that mattered.

Whether Arthur won or lost playing for the UCLA Bruins, he was news. Only Althea Gibson, winner of the 1957 and 1958 women's singles title at Wimbledon, had captured the headlines for black athletes in tennis before Ashe arrived. "Tennis has always been dominated by whites," observed one California sports columnist. "But this Arthur Ashe at UCLA is clearly one to watch on the courts. He's got the moves of a champion."

Naturally, Arthur enjoyed much of the hype. Who wouldn't? Yet it also put greater responsibility on his shoulders. He became more and more aware that he was not merely representing himself, his family, and UCLA. He was representing his race. What he did, on or off the court, reflected upon blacks across the nation. In the early 1960s, Martin Luther King, Jr., and other civil rights leaders were pushing hard to gain equality for blacks. Like it or not, in his own small way, Arthur Ashe was a part of this movement.

Arthur got a nasty taste of racial prejudice tossed in his face by the Balboa Bay Club in Orange County, California. The club hosted a tennis tournament of college teams, including UCLA, but Ashe was not invited because the organization did not admit blacks.

Charlie Pasarell, Arthur's roommate and UCLA's number one player, wanted no part of the Balboa Bay Club tournament. Neither did Coach Morgan. But Ashe was reluctant to be the center of attention in this unpleasant situation. Maybe later, when and if he had achieved fame, he would make a difference. For now, Ashe encouraged his teammates to join in and wallop the daylights out of their opponents. (In later years, the Balboa Bay Club *did* invite Arthur to play tournaments. Then it was Arthur who cheerfully refused the club's offer.)

But if the Balboa Bay Club incident was a slap in the face, the pro at the Beverly Hills Tennis Club offered Arthur a pat on the back. Pancho Gonzales was Arthur's first tennis idol; and when the UCLA student discovered he could go and watch him play, Ashe was delighted. Soon they were opponents on the court, and Arthur soaked up every tip Gonzales offered.

"From the first time I saw him play, I knew Arthur Ashe was destined for success as a tennis champion," Gonzales recalled later. "He was never satisfied with his performance, always feeling he could do better. That's the sign of a champion."

As a sophomore at UCLA, Arthur captured the top title in the Southern California Sectional competition. This intercollegiate victory qualified him for Wimbledon, the world's most prestigious tennis tournament, held each summer in England. However, a major obstacle stood in Arthur's way: money. Travel and expenses would run about $800. Arthur knew his family could not afford a trip to England.

Enter a fairy godmother.

Arthur was playing an exhibition match at the California Club in west Los Angeles in April 1963.

Seated in the stands was a club member named Julianna Ogner. After the match was over, the players mingled with the spectators, and Ogner asked Arthur about his summer plans. He spoke about his prospects of competing at Wimbledon but added that it was only a possibility because of the financing. The problem was quickly solved. Julianna Ogner, impressed with both Arthur's playing and his manners, offered to put up the money. Stunned, Arthur could barely stammer his thanks.

Wimbledon. It was the dream of every serious young tennis player. Arthur chuckled as he wondered what the Balboa Bay Club would have to say about this.

Chapter / Five

Battles to Fight

At nineteen, Arthur Ashe had never been out of the United States. In heading to Wimbledon, he was reaching the goal sought by tennis players around the world. Nearly every year since 1877, the world's finest tennis players had been competing at the games held by the All-England Lawn Tennis and Croquet Club. The internationally rich and famous—kings and queens, princes and princesses—all made their annual trek to the London suburb to witness the best the sport had to offer. They watched the top tennis players do battle for the honor of taking home the shining Wimbledon Cup.

"Of course, I had no thought of winning," Ashe recalled later. "Just being there was beyond my wildest dreams. I decided I would simply do my best and enjoy every moment."

From the moment he got off his plane at the London airport, Arthur felt caught up in the grand tradition of Wimbledon. He was transported in style each day from his hotel to the courts by a sleek new Bentley. Everywhere he looked there was green—green chairs, green ivy climbing on walls, green doors and balconies, green buttons and banners. The umpires wore hard straw hats and carnations, maintaining a nearly century-old tradition. All the pageantry and magnificence dazzled the UCLA visitor.

While Arthur enjoyed the grandeur of his surroundings, the Wimbledon crowd sized him up also. As historic as the Wimbledon matches were to be that year, by his mere presence Arthur Ashe was writing another page in the tournament archives. Few black men had displayed their talents on those cherished courts. Just how would the young man fare? people wondered.

In his first contest, Arthur relied on his standard serve-and-volley skills. Carlos Fernandes of Brazil was no match for the pounding power of his American opponent. After a victory in three straight sets, Ashe felt relaxed and confident. But the next contest was not so easy. John Hillebrand from Australia offered a seesaw battle that took the match to five sets, leaving Arthur an exhausted victor. "They can't be much tougher than this one," a newspaper quoted him as saying.

Arthur spoke a bit too soon. Next he faced fellow American Chuck McKinley, a student at Trinity University in Texas who was ranked number one in the States. The two had played against each other before, and Arthur knew he would be lucky to get past the quick and snappy fireball. From the moment the match began, McKinley dominated the action. "No Mercy McKinley," one sports columnist dubbed the champion, who blasted Arthur off the court in straight sets. Offering no excuses, Ashe simply smiled. "The better man won," he remarked, and then headed for the showers. McKinley went on to win the men's singles Wimbledon tournament without dropping a set.

Returning to America, Arthur shook off the Wimbledon loss and headed for Chicago to take part in the U.S. Hardcourt championships. Although he preferred grass or concrete surfaces, Ashe displayed a more versatile style and managed to dump top-seeded Chris Crawford to take the tournament.

Within a week after the Chicago matches, Arthur faced Chuck McKinley again. At the Merion Cricket Club outside Philadelphia, the

UCLA underdog grabbed a commanding lead, thanks to a serve that sped and spun past the surprised McKinley. No one was more amazed than Ashe himself, who captured the first set, 6-1. By the second set, however, the Wimbledon champ regained his poise and returned to the blazing performance that had left his overseas audience in awe. Yet people were talking about Arthur Ashe, too, and he was ranked number six in the country. A berth on the Davis Cup team became a strong possibility.

But Arthur's hopes dimmed when he failed to capture the top spot at the Eastern Grass Court championships at South Orange, New Jersey. Able to control opponent Gene Scott's power serve at the beginning of the match, Ashe began slamming returns into the net as the contest progressed. Usually quiet on the court, Arthur yelled at himself for missing shots. A final slap into the net sent a disgusted Ashe to the showers.

Strangely enough, Arthur learned later that same day that he'd been picked to play for the Davis Cup team. Some observers were skeptical when Gene Scott was ignored for the squad. Had the power of the civil rights movement reached into the world of tennis? Was Arthur Ashe selected because of his color or his talent?

To Arthur, the answer was obvious. "Just check the won and lost record," he told a reporter.

There was no doubt in the mind of the coach of the Davis Cup team, either. Pancho Gonzales knew just how talented Arthur was. He'd been playing him for years.

The team trained hard. Every minute of each day was devoted to building strength and stamina. A bacon-and-eggs breakfast (considered very healthful then) at eight started each day. Cereal and milk (skim for everybody but Arthur—he needed whole milk because of his slender build), maybe some fruit, followed. Then it was off to run and lift weights, perhaps chop wood. Skipping rope was encouraged. Then came an hour or two of practice on the courts. At lunch, meat and fruit were the entree choices, milk the beverage. A rest period followed, with TV-watching allowed, a game of cards, a nap. By two o'clock, the players were back on the courts, perfecting their shots, pounding their serves, slicing, twisting, and turning under Coach Gonzales's careful eye. Sweat dripped from foreheads, soaked into T-shirts and shorts. By six, dinner was on the table and team members wolfed down steak or roast beef, plenty of vegetables. No bread or biscuits, though. Too heavy in the belly. Most of the players turned in early, long before the midnight "lights out" curfew. After all, the routine would be starting all over again in a few hours.

The tough conditioning program paid off in Davis Cup action. Whenever and wherever they played, the American squad dominated the courts in 1963. Nervously, Arthur Ashe waited his turn to compete. It was different from playing for himself or for a school. Davis Cup players were representing their country. Participation touched the players' special sense of patriotism. For Ashe, the feeling went even beyond that. Confident that he had been picked for his tennis rather than his color, he still felt the added weight of racism on his shoulders. He was a black man. To some in America, that was equated simply with being another human being. To others, a black man was a "nigger." Maybe, just maybe, by playing well and being a gentleman, he might change people's attitudes here and there. The sound of "nigger" might become a whisper, or the ugly word might even vanish into the wind . . .

In Davis Cup action, five matches are played, four singles and one doubles. Arthur's chance came in Denver, Colorado, when the Americans took on the Venezuelans. By the time Ashe arrived on the court, his team had already won three matches, assuring the victory. But when Orlando Bracamonte appeared on the other side of the net, Arthur stood ready to do battle. After all, this was for his country, his people, and himself.

In the match that followed, Arthur played his heart out. His serve rocketed over the net, leaving Bracamonte dumbfounded. Bracamonte scrambled to make returns, yet more than once lay flat on his face. His own shots found Ashe's racket always in position and ready to return the ball just out of the Venezuelan's reach. It was Ashe's match from start to finish. Bracamonte managed to wrangle wins in only two games out of three sets, afterward remarking, "I was lucky to get those."

By the opening of the 1964 tennis season at UCLA, Ashe occupied the number one position and was also one of the squad captains. In the national amateur rankings, he was number six. A favorite among newspaper and magazine journalists, he was often featured in sports copy. In a country still stunned by the assassination of President John F. Kennedy late in 1963, Arthur Ashe had a calming effect. While militant civil rights leaders like Malcolm X, H. Rap Brown, and Stokely Carmichael demanded immediate changes for blacks, Ashe took a different philosophy.

"I think progress takes place a step at a time," Arthur told one reporter. "Pacing is important. One

can try to do too much too fast, just like in tennis. A player who puts everything into the first game or two of a set comes up short at the end. I'm a pacer. I know I would fail if I tried to be something I'm not."

In college action that season, the spotlight was on Arthur and Dennis Ralston, the sparkling star of the University of Southern California. (UCLA and USC were bitter crosstown rivals in all sports they played.) Ralston was ranked number one on the Pacific Coast, while Ashe held down the number two slot.

But on the courts it was anybody's game. Only professional players drew bigger crowds than the two California rivals. Spectators never came away disappointed as the two mighty men of collegiate tennis waged power wars that lasted two and three hours. Sometimes Ashe took top honors; at other times Ralston walked away the winner. The topflight competition polished Arthur's game. When he headed for Wimbledon in June 1964, Ashe was a fine-tuned instrument, ready for action.

In opening Wimbledon play, Arthur faced Milan Holecek from Czechoslovakia. The match went to Ashe. Next he took on Cliff Richey from Texas. Again the match went to Ashe. Another American, Bill Bond, stepped forward to challenge

Lean and long, Arthur plays breathtaking tennis against Orlando Bracamonte.

Arthur. Another win for Ashe. Three up, three
down. Next, please?

Next was Australian superstar Roy Emerson.
Arthur entertained few thoughts of upsetting the
world's top amateur player. Even as he walked onto
the court, he realized his chances were slim. "I
knew I would take away something from playing
this guy," Ashe recalled later. "Often, when I have
little hope of pulling out a win, I go into the match
to learn. I think it's being realistic rather than pes-
simistic. Naturally, there's always a bit of optimism
present, too, that a miracle could happen."

There were no miracles that day. Emerson blis-
tered the ball with each serve and shot, sending
Arthur racing to every spot on the court. Smoke
seemed to come out of Emerson's racket. Ashe
fought back, but there was never a chance to take
the offensive. Emerson won the match in straight
sets, going on to knock off the defending
Wimbledon champion, Chuck McKinley, to capture the tournament cup.

The veteran of two Wimbledons now, Ashe
returned to the United States with no shame at
either of his performances. After all, each time he
had fallen to the eventual winner, Chuck McKinley
or Roy Emerson.

In the Pennsylvania Grass Court championships, McKinley again became Ashe's opponent in the finals action. Fresh from his bout with Emerson, Arthur was stronger than ever. In a two-out-of-three match, Ashe blasted away at his nemesis. There were no lopsided games this time, with McKinley barely managing to squeak out victories that ran 10-8, 10-8. "Is this the same Arthur Ashe I played before?" McKinley observed afterward. "Somebody must have supercharged his batteries."

On to South Orange, New Jersey, where Ashe competed in the Eastern Grass Court championships. This time he faced another old rival, Dennis Ralston, for the title. The titan from southern California won the first match in a 15-13 nip-and-tuck exchange, but then Arthur took charge. Wondering if he could even last another set or two of twenty-eight games, Arthur pounded his serve into Ralston, following with long, hard drives to the baseline. It was too much for the Californian. Ashe swept the next two sets easily and won the match. Next he played one more longtime tennis foe, Gene Scott. This time it was all Ashe, who beat Scott in straight sets. Only Clark Graebner stood in Arthur's way for the Eastern Grass Court title.

"Only" should be changed. Graebner proved a worthy challenger, meeting Ashe's power with strong shots of his own. After Graebner captured the first set, 6-4, he relaxed just a bit. Like a vulture, Arthur swooped, grabbing away the next three sets, 6-4, 6-4, and 6-3.

There were no questions raised about Arthur Ashe being selected for the Davis Cup team now. He jumped into the rigid training program, ready to give his best when needed. Although the American squad lost its Challenge Round against Australia, 3-2, Ashe emerged a winner anyway. He captured the Johnston Award, the top tennis prize in the United States, given to a player who displays not only quality tennis talent but courtesy, character, and a spirit of cooperation. Standing before packed bleachers in Cleveland, Ohio, Ashe smiled. "I hope I can prove to be the exception to the rule that 'good guys always finish last,'" he joked. The audience rose to their feet and applauded. Few people, if any, doubted that Arthur's words would come true.

Chapter / Six

Net Gains and Losses

Not only did the Johnston Award recognize tennis talent and personal character; it carried with it the understanding that its recipient would help future tennis enthusiasts. No one took that challenge more seriously than Arthur Ashe. Whenever he played for UCLA or in general tournament competition, he looked around for young people. His entire face lit up whenever he spotted a black boy or girl carrying a racket. "Want to hit a few balls?" he would ask. Often the answer was "Sure." When the moment was right and his partner receptive, Arthur offered useful hints. The boy or girl would walk away smiling. Arthur would smile, too, grateful for the chance to help.

"I knew what Jackie Robinson did when he became the first black to play major league baseball," Ashe observed. "Willie Mays did his part, too. In basketball, it was Bill Russell and Wilt Chamberlain. Jimmy Brown tore up the football field, and Gale Sayers. I figured if I could do a little bit in tennis, it might help some."

By the end of 1964, Arthur was ranked the number three collegiate player in the country, right behind Dennis Ralston and Chuck McKinley. He had played both of them—and beaten them—but they had run him off the court a few times, too. Ashe was pleased with his placement. But just like anyone else who is ranked nationally, he knew that everybody was after him. Whatever tournament he entered, he was fair game to be knocked off.

Sometimes he *was* defeated. At first it bothered Arthur a lot. Then he became resigned to the fact that eager challengers pushed themselves hard when they knew they might be playing him. When they did meet him on the court, they were superhyped, their adrenaline flowing nonstop. They took risks with their shots. What did they have to lose? Giving up a match to the number three collegiate tennis player in the country was no disgrace. Some days Arthur handled the assaults well. At other times he succumbed. He admitted to his personal weaknesses.

"Quality tennis demands 100 percent of your

Arthur gladly does his bit for kids at a tennis clinic.

physical and mental energy," Arthur observed. "There are days when I slide by, just trying to win. My mind wanders. Catch me on one of those days and you've got me beat."

Some tennis enthusiasts wondered whether Arthur had the staying power of a true champion. Maybe he was a fluke, a hit-and-run kid who sparkled for a while, then dimmed.

But Arthur squelched those rumors with his play in the preliminary 1965 Davis Cup competition. To compete in the final summer action, a nation had to beat the opponents in its own geographical zone. The United States faced Canada. Arthur carried his country's honor well, blasting away Canadians Keith Carpenter and Harry Fauquier. The other Davis Cup team members followed Ashe's lead, whipping their Canadian opponents to win the American Zone title.

Psyched up and playing well, Arthur returned to UCLA to take part in the National Collegiate Athletic Association competition. Under a warm June sun and blue skies, Ashe snagged the singles title, hardly needing a second wind. In doubles action, he teamed up with Ian Crookenden to capture the doubles trophy. Newspaper headlines dubbed Arthur the "King of College Tennis."

Wimbledon was now a yearly summer outing for Arthur, yet he never really entertained hopes of winning the tournament. The recent National Collegiate victories built up his confidence, however. Maybe this year would be his turn. He breezed through his first three matches. Then he encountered Rafael Osuña of Mexico. Ashe had beaten Osuña before, but this time the light-footed Mexican could not be stopped. He took Ashe in three sets, 8-6, 6-4, 6-4.

Disappointed, Arthur returned to America and threw himself into tournament action. The cold spell continued. Try as he might, Ashe could not recapture his victory pattern. Returning to the Davis Cup team, Ashe felt even greater pressure to win. The United States faced Mexico in competition in Dallas, Texas. Drawings were held for singles position, and who should come up as Ashe's first opponent? Rafael Osuña. "When I heard that, I wanted to heave my racket a mile," Ashe admitted.

Thanks to Coach Pancho Gonzales and team captain George McCall, Ashe entered the match against Osuña with a positive attitude. "They'd convinced me I could win," said Ashe, "so who was I to argue?" From the first serve, there was no argument from anyone. Arthur's rocketing serve left a befuddled Osuña standing helpless. Scoring fifteen service aces, Ashe won the match, 6-2, 6-3, and 9-7. The revenge for the Wimbledon encounter was sweet indeed.

Two days later, Ashe returned to take on Antonio Palafox. Once more Arthur's serve boomed across the net, bringing him ace after ace. The 6-1, 6-4, 6-4 shellacking pitted the United States against Spain in the Interzone finals. However, since the matches were scheduled for the clay courts in Barcelona, Ashe was not asked to make the trip. It was true that clay surfaces were not Ashe's favorite. Still, he seemed to have earned the right to go.

No matter. Arthur headed into the U.S.

Nationals competition at Forest Hills, New York.
Once again, he found himself paired against an old
adversary—Roy Emerson. Eleven thousand fans
came to watch the action. It wasn't often that people could see a Davis Cup star take on a Wimbledon champ. Emerson was favored, but no one
counted Ashe out. The two battled, point for point,
neither player letting up a bit. The first set found
Arthur pulling out a narrow victory, 13-11.
Although his cannonball serve wasn't working well,
his ground strokes sent the ball speeding just over
the net, pulling Emerson in, then pushing him
away. After almost three hours of power tennis,
Ashe emerged the champion, three sets to one.

Slipping past Emerson, Arthur assumed the
tournament was his. Yet Manuel Santana of Spain
had ideas of his own. Most people thought Santana
would have trouble with the clay courts. For one
set, he did. But once he settled in, Ashe could not
keep up with the sure-shot Spaniard. Santana beat
Ashe, 2-6, 6-4, 6-2, and 6-4. "Sure, losing to
Santana was a big disappointment," Arthur
recalled, "but proving I could beat Emerson lifted
my confidence a lot."

Back at UCLA, Arthur got his credits together
in preparation for graduation the following spring.
He intended to swing down to Australia with the

Davis Cup team for a tournament tour, yet he wanted to make sure his classwork was in order. "Arthur was unique in many ways," one of his professors recalled. "Many of our athletes place their sport first and their studies a distant second. Arthur Ashe had a great deal of respect for learning. Due to his active sports program, he couldn't complete his requirements right on schedule. But he never asked for special favors."

Once in Australia, Ashe discovered that he was famous. Part of his celebrity status came from the fact that tennis is Australia's national sport. As the number-six-ranked tennis player in the world, Arthur was a superstar. The fact that he was an African American set him in a league of his own, too, because there are few blacks in Australia. Ashe gave the Australians their money's worth, copping top honors at the Queensland championships in Brisbane and reaching the finals at the New South Wales tournament. "This fellow Ashe puts on a bloody good show," observed one newscaster. "He's mastered our game quite nicely."

Returning to the United States, Arthur accepted a special invitation. February 4, 1966, was officially declared Arthur Ashe Day in Richmond, Virginia. The folks in Arthur's hometown wanted to honor him in style. Unbelievable! As a boy he had stood behind fences watching other kids play tennis on courts he could not set foot on because he was black. He couldn't compete in tournaments because of his color, either, or live in certain neighborhoods or go to certain schools. Now Arthur stayed in the best hotel, dined at an elegant banquet, and heard the mayor and other officials sing his praises. Ron Charity and Dr. Johnson spoke, too, and of course Arthur Ashe, Sr., wore a smile that wouldn't quit. Times had changed. "Ten years ago this would not have happened," said Arthur to those honoring him. "It is as much a tribute to Richmond and the state of Virginia as it is to me."

Most people assumed Arthur Ashe would jump into the professional tennis circuit after he graduated from UCLA in June 1966. His commitment to the army, through his ROTC duties, wasn't well-known. With his diploma still fresh in his hand, Arthur traveled to Fort Lewis, Washington, to begin his two years of military service. His ROTC training at UCLA won him an appointment as deputy brigade commander during his six weeks of boot camp. After being formally inducted into the army in July, he was offered the chance to help coach tennis at the U.S. Military Academy at West Point, New York. "Sounds good to me," said a smiling Arthur Ashe. He'd doubted whether he would

A *special homecoming: Arthur accepts a plaque from Richmond's mayor commemorating Arthur Ashe Day.*

have much time for tennis or tournaments while in the army. This was a perfect opportunity.

Arthur liked working with other players at West Point, honing their strokes, strengthening their serves, pointing out their strong and weak points. But juggling the duties of an army second lieutenant and a tennis coach proved exhausting. "I wasn't in the service for my own purposes," said Ashe. "It was a responsibility for my country, a debt I owed."

He knew his own tennis game would slip, and

it did. There was no Wimbledon competition for him in 1966 and 1967, and no U.S. Nationals championships, either. But he made it to the finals of the U.S. Indoor championships in 1966 and copped the U.S. Clay Court championship trophy in 1967.

As he neared his release from the army in 1968, Arthur longed for the full-time competition of tennis. With the help of writer Clifford Gewecke, Jr., Ashe wrote his autobiography *Advantage Ashe,* especially aimed at black youths. "I hope there's a black kid somewhere who will push a little harder after reading the book," said Arthur. "Sometimes it seems like you're battling against the wind, but with God's help and your own effort, that wind will change."

Chapter / Seven

Facing New Challenges

After a two-year absence, Arthur Ashe returned to Wimbledon. The colorful trappings were in place, the historical spectacle was still in motion, yet there had been a major change. Up until 1968, Wimbledon competition had been open only to amateur players. This was true of other major tournaments, too. Therefore, the pros played the pros, and the amateurs took on amateurs. Tennis enthusiasts could only imagine what might happen if a particular professional player went up against a particular amateur player.

That all changed in March 1968, when the International Tennis Federation (ITF) rewrote the rules. The restrictions crumbled. Now the entry field for Wimbledon and most of the other tennis tournaments was wide open. The Davis Cup competition remained closed to professionals, though.

Arthur reached England with an impressive array of Davis Cup victories, six in all, and he was eager for Wimbledon action. Being seeded number thirteen brought the recently discharged army man mixed reactions. "I didn't expect to be so high," Ashe said, "and although I'm not superstitious, number thirteen is not a sign of *good* luck, is it?"

It seemed to be, the way Arthur started his Wimbledon play that June. In straight-set victories, he knocked off Eduardo Zuleta, Ismail El Shafei, and Ove Bengston. Then Ashe ran into John Newcombe, the reigning Wimbledon and U.S. Nationals champion. Both men depended on a strong serve-and-volley game, but Newcombe engaged in a psychological contest, trying to fake his opponent out. Concentration had always been a weakness in Arthur's playing.

As the two men took the court and started playing, Ashe kept his head every moment. Serves sizzled inches above the net; shots landed just inside boundaries on both sides. Back and forth the ball flew, banging against each racket and hurling its way like a bullet. After two sets, Ashe forced a smile. He was winning, 6-4, 6-4. Then Newcombe caught fire, grabbing sets three and four with scores of 6-1 and 6-4. Ashe focused on Newcombe's every move, edging to his right with a threatened power backhand to Newcombe's serve. The strategy paid off, and Ashe took the final set, 6-3.

Next Arthur faced the Netherlands' Tom Okker, whose nickname, the "Flying Dutchman," suggested his ability to whiz around the court with superspeed. The tennis jet darted here and there and always seemed able to return the ball. At the end of the first set, Ashe was sweating, having dropped the opening round, 7-9. The advice of coaches past pounded into his mind. "Keep your eye on the ball, not the opponent. Concentrate. Concentrate." When Arthur returned to the court, he joined the Dutchman's running match, emerging the victor, 9-7, 9-7, 6-2.

In semifinal action on July 5, Ashe took on southpaw Rod Laver. Nothing could stand in the way of the mighty Australian's march to victory. Despite all Arthur's efforts, Laver polished him off, 7-5, 6-2, 6-4. Two days later, Laver hoisted the Wimbledon cup as the tournament winner.

Losing is never a cheerful occasion, but satisfaction sometimes can be found in an athlete's performance. Such was Ashe's frame of mind when he returned from England. The stint in the military had limited his competitive efforts, yet he felt good about his Wimbledon performances. The

American press added to his sense of well-being. "Would that we could always send an Arthur Ashe abroad to represent us in a sport," one midwestern editor wrote. "Not only does he excel in what he does, he excels in how he does it. He may not be bringing home the Wimbledon championship, but he still comes home a champion." Such words took a bit of the sting out of losing.

But Arthur still hungered to win a major tournament. As he rejoined the Davis Cup team, he posted two victories that helped defeat Spain in the Interzone competition. He headed on to Brookline, Massachusetts, for the U.S. Nationals championships. His appetite to win increased, and he blasted away five opponents and entered the finals. Bob Lutz, a Davis Cup pal, blocked his path to the title.

But nothing could prevent Arthur from winning the prize. Not ninety-degree temperatures. Not a match that ran fifty-three games. Nothing. Beating Bob Lutz set Arthur up as the number one amateur in the nation.

Traveling to Forest Hills, Ashe savored the taste of victory and wanted more. It was the first U.S. Open. When he learned that his father and Dr. Johnson were going to be in the stands, Arthur wanted to win all the more. His tennis competition prevented him from spending as much time with his family as he would have liked. Playing in front of his father was a special thrill.

Arthur's early foes at Forest Hills, including Roy Emerson, were formidable, but Ashe rolled over them easily in straight sets. South Africa's Cliff Drysdale proved a bit more of a challenge, as did Davis Cup teammate Clark Graebner. Eventually only one player stood in his way—Tom Okker. It would not be a Wimbledon repeat, according to the Flying Dutchman. "This time it's my turn to win," Okker told reporters.

Rain delays postponed the finals of the U.S. Open until September 9. From the opening serve, it was clear that both men planned a slow, steady tempo of action. Back and forth, back and forth the ball flew. Game for Ashe. Game for Okker. Each man won his own serve and lost his opponent's. Finally, Arthur broke the Flying Dutchman's service in the twenty-sixth game and won the set, 14-12. "Just that one set felt like an entire match," said Arthur Ashe, Sr., after the initial play ended. "I wondered if the two of them had any strength left to continue."

They did indeed, with Okker taking the second set, 7-5, to even up the battle. Ashe had an easier time with set three, winning it 6-3. But just when Okker seemed down, he won the fourth set, 6-3. Plopping into a chair, Arthur felt totally drained. His one-pound racket seemed like a heavy shovel. His head throbbed; his eyes burned from the scorching sun. But there could be no substitutions, no time out. One more set to go.

Ashe took the court, remembering his father and Dr. Johnson in the stands. He took a 4-2 game advantage. Next, he pounded at Okker's backhand, winning another game. Finally, after over two hours of play, he served like a cannon. Okker stood shocked. Where could all this power be coming from at this stage of the match? Ashe won the match, 6-3, raced to shake his opponent's hand, and ran into his father's outstretched arms. "Winner of the first U.S. Open—Arthur Ashe." That sounded mighty fine! Not only that, but he became the first black man to win a Grand Slam tournament.

Anyone who had questioned Arthur Ashe's staying power in the tennis arena no longer did so. Arthur was a major power in the sport, no doubt about it. Only the 1968 Davis Cup finals lay before him.

In November the American squad traveled to Puerto Rico, where the players faced a determined team from India. Ashe defeated Premjit Lall and

Arthur Ashe, Sr., is visibly moved after watching his son win the first U.S. Open.

Ramnathan Krishnan, setting the pace for his teammates. After the win over India, it was on to Adelaide, Australia, for the finals.

The Aussies were playing without several of their top stars. Roy Emerson, Rod Laver, John Newcombe, and Ken Rosewall were all professionals and ineligible. The Australian bunch were young and inexperienced, but the American squad took nothing for granted. "A lot of matches, key matches, have been lost by being overly confident," recalled Ashe. Clark Graebner racked up the first win for the United States, and Arthur followed his lead. If only the doubles team of Stan Smith and Bob Lutz could win, the United States would take home the coveted cup. Too nervous to watch, Graebner and Ashe drove around Adelaide listening to the competition on the car radio. With each point scored by the U.S. team, Graebner and Ashe went wild, pounding each other and cheering. Slowly, steadily, the American twosome pulled away. "We've done it! We've won!" the men in the car shouted. No doubt, Australian onlookers thought the sight more than a bit strange. But Ashe and Graebner were beyond caring. They had helped bring back the Davis Cup to their own country. "It felt better than the individual tournament wins I had that year," said Arthur. "Winning

something for your country transcends any personal accomplishment."

The U.S. Davis Cup team took the long way
home. America was at war, engaged in the Vietnam
struggle, and soldiers eagerly welcomed their country's tennis champs in hospitals and military units
throughout Southeast Asia. Arthur even met a few
of his former players from his days at West Point.

"Great goin', Coach!" a soldier called out.

"Same to you, buddy!" Ashe hollered back. If
time allowed, he stopped to visit.

President Lyndon Baines Johnson welcomed
the team to the White House when the players
returned to the States. "Individually and collec-
tively, you have brought pride to our nation," said
the chief executive. The words thrilled twenty-five-
year-old Arthur Ashe. The black boy from
Richmond had come a long way from the days of
swatting around a ball at Brook Field Park. Now he
was ranked number one tennis player in the nation.
His face graced the magazine covers of *Life* and
Sports Illustrated. Wherever he traveled, radio and
television people begged for interviews. In the
world of journalistic jargon, Arthur Ashe was "hot
copy," and reporters sought him eagerly. Officials at
Head USA wanted to market an Arthur Ashe
racket, and, with Catalina, they planned to bring

out Ashe tennis wear. Coca-Cola and American Express offered to set up tennis clinics using his name. The cash registers jingled and Arthur's bank account grew. He rented an apartment in the ritzy Upper East Side of New York City. When he could, he took a date to a concert or a Broadway play.

A sore elbow slowed Arthur's tennis action in 1969, but could not slow his activity. He watched as the popularity of tennis skyrocketed around the world. In many places it became a family sport, drawing parents and children to the courts. New apartment complexes and schools included tennis courts. Television networks fought for the rights to broadcast tournaments.

Despite the popularity of tennis, however, players were concerned. Football and basketball players received multimillion-dollar contracts. By comparison, prize money for winning tennis tournaments remained at paltry levels.

To protect the rights of tennis players, Arthur helped form the International Tennis Players Association (ITPA). As its treasurer, Arthur joined others in speaking out on a variety of public issues, such as improved financial status of players and their rights to play where and when they wished.

When Arthur applied for a visa to visit South Africa in 1969, he was refused. Why? South African officials claimed Ashe was antagonistic to the nation's racial policies. "If they mean am I opposed to apartheid, yes, I would have to admit I am," Ashe declared. "But I'm not going there to overthrow the government. I just want to play in the South African Open." The visa refusal helped to cast the world spotlight on the white-black conflict in South Africa. Responding to the government's action, Ashe called for the country to be banned from Davis Cup competition and expelled from the ITF.

In February 1970, an announcement was made that South Africa was indeed ineligible for Davis Cup competition. "That action made me aware that perhaps I did have some personal power in how things happened," said Ashe. "I'd never thought of myself as a political activist, yet that is exactly what I was becoming."

The U.S. government helped Ashe in his cause by applying political pressure. Arthur was appointed a goodwill ambassador to Africa and joined Stan Smith, the new number-one-ranked tennis star, on a tour of the continent. It was an exciting journey, meeting with government officials and college students, picking their brains, and sharing new ideas. At a visit to a Cameroon tennis club, Arthur spotted a young player, Yannick Noah, displaying fan-

Arthur in January 1970. By now the top-ranking U.S. tennis player, he has also become a political activist, protesting South Africa's policy of apartheid.

tastic shots and amazing poise on the courts. Ashe arranged for the French Tennis Federation to take the eleven-year-old boy under its wing. By the time he was twenty, Noah was ranked number one in France. "It felt good to be able to help," said Arthur.

In 1972, the ITPA became the ATP, the Association of Tennis Professionals. The change in title did not, however, affect the organization's goal to protect the rights of players. When Yugoslavia ordered Nikki Pilic to play for its Davis Cup team or else not play at Wimbledon, Ashe called for all ATP players to avoid the Wimbledon tournament. The ATP members agreed, and the Wimbledon tournament of 1973 was less than a world competition. Within months, Yugoslavia changed its policy.

Arthur continued his campaign against the policies of South Africa while annually requesting entrance to play in its respected tournament. After four visa requests and denials, suddenly his application went through. When he refused to travel as an "honorary white"—the status South African officials assigned to him—the government again gave in to him. "I won't play tennis before a segregated audience," he also insisted. So be it, the South Africans agreed. "And I want to travel where I please and say what I want." Once more, the South

African government offered no challenge. No doubt those in power were looking ahead to the 1976 Olympic Games. They wanted no trouble for their own athletes who planned to compete.

Arthur was criticized for his decision to go to South Africa. "Why does he go where he's not wanted?" some black leaders asked. When he answered that he thought he could help the blacks there, critics hurled another charge. "You're helping blacks in Africa? What about the blacks in your own country? They need help, too."

At times it seemed hopeless to Arthur. He was one person, the only influential black person in American tennis. No matter how carefully he planned his moves, there was criticism.

People jammed Ellis Park in Johannesburg to watch the South African Open. The black spectators cheered loudly for Ashe as he blasted away his opponents. But another American, Jimmy Connors, knocked Ashe out in the final round. Disappointed but undaunted, Arthur teamed up with his longtime rival Tom Okker, and the two of them captured the doubles crown. "In a way, this might have been the most important doubles match I ever won," Arthur wrote later, "for now a black's name rests on the list of South African champions. Etched. Forever."

ATP business took more of Arthur's time once he stepped into the shoes of president of the organization. He was glad to see players cutting better deals with tournament organizers and the media. Cash prizes had increased, conditions for clinics had improved, and tennis was wearing a new look. But for Ashe personally, the changes meant spending many more hours signing papers or giving speeches. Sports reporters whispered that maybe Arthur Ashe was through on the court.

That wasn't exactly Arthur's game plan.

Chapter / Eight

Reaching New Heights

In the mid-1970s, Arthur slipped gracefully into his thirties, very much aware that a new group of young tennis stars were pounding the ball and making their presence felt. Jimmy Connors excited fans and riled officials everywhere he played and often walked away with tournament titles. A less boisterous player, a solid ground stroker and power server from Sweden, Bjorn Borg seemed to have ice in his veins yet fire in his hands as he blasted away opponent after opponent. Not only did Connors and Borg possess the speed reserved for the young, but they perfected the passing shot. Anyone thinking of approaching the net did so knowing the ball could come sizzling past.

In early 1975, Ashe went on a full-fledged physical fitness binge. He hired a coach, Harry

Hines, to help him get in shape. Together they flew to Puerto Rico, where Arthur would tone up his body.

Running and lifting weights eased away the minor pains and kinks. Arthur watched every bite of food he took in, balanced his fluids, too, and made sure he got plenty of sleep. His walk took on a fresh spring, and his eyes sparkled behind the dark-framed glasses. On the court, he perfected a collection of dink shots. If he couldn't maintain the speed of the younger challengers, he could place his shots better. It was a typical step for an older competitor.

In the spring of 1975, Arthur attended a reception for promising black college and university students in Washington, D.C. He smiled as Thurgood Marshall, the first African American to serve on the U.S. Supreme Court, approached and extended his hand.

"You're a tremendous role model for black youth," Justice Marshall said. "I hope we'll be watching you play tennis for a long time to come."

Those words meant a lot to Arthur Ashe. In the following weeks they echoed in his mind, spurring him on to tougher workouts.

The World Championship Tennis competition in Dallas, Texas, beckoned him in May. A heel injury proved troublesome going into the competition, but Ashe never considered dropping out. No, he had worked too hard. After all, if he were to give in to the slightest bump or bruise, he'd probably never play again. At almost thirty-two, Arthur realized he would never again have the body of a twenty-year-old. But he could still play quality tennis!

If Arthur was troubled by his heel during the opening matches of WCT play, it didn't show. He sped around the court, chipping, slicing, blasting away at the ball. Spectators sat amazed. It was the old Arthur Ashe, playing his best. His super-caliber performance put him into the finals against Bjorn Borg. The Swede's icy calm and fiery strokes, however, were useless against the dazzling Ashe. To the net, back to the baseline, to the right side, then the left, Arthur was everywhere at once, placing the ball with power and precision. At the end of the match, Borg gave a quick bow to the WCT champion, then exited the court. A smiling Ashe stepped forward to accept his rewards, which included a solid-gold tennis ball worth $33,000.

That summer Arthur headed to Wimbledon with new resolve. If ever he was going to capture this tournament prize, it was now. He felt good, the win over Borg offering him new confidence. He was determined to win.

When the tournament opened on June 23, regular Wimbledon fans noticed Arthur's freshness and speed. He disposed of his first opponent, Bob Hewitt, 7-5, 3-6, 6-2, 6-4. Next it was Jun Kamiwazumi, 6-2, 7-5, 6-4. Brian Gottfried was the third to fall, 6-2, 6-3, 6-1. Number four to tumble under the Ashe attack was Graham Stilwell, a British favorite, who lost 6-2, 5-7, 6-4, 6-2. "There were rumors that Arthur Ashe was still nursing a heel disorder coming to Wimbledon," observed one London sports columnist. "If that is true, the remaining contenders might hurry out and get one too. Ashe is playing splendid tennis!"

"Splendid tennis" is exactly what Arthur knew he had to play to beat Bjorn Borg again. Arthur got off to a slow start, losing the first set to the Swedish star, 2-6. Shifting his game plan, Ashe made a comeback in the second set, pulling it out 6-4. The third set was a real free-for-all, with Ashe squeaking by, 8-6. It was smooth sailing after that, and Arthur coasted to a final-set win of 6-1.

Arthur faced Australian Tony Roche in semifinal competition. Roche had beaten Ashe earlier that year, so Arthur knew the match would be tough. His premonition was right on target. The scrappy Roche wouldn't give up. It took five sets, 5-7, 6-4, 7-5, 8-9, 6-4, to turn the determined

Aussie away.

One man was left: fellow American Jimmy Connors. A battling and brash left-handed fireball from Belleville, Illinois, Connors was tearing up the courts. The year before, he had won Wimbledon, the U.S. Open, and thirteen other major tournaments. In their three previous encounters, Connors had won every time. He was some ten years younger than Ashe and a 3-20 odds favorite among Wimbledon spectators.

Although Arthur respected Connors as a fine tennis player, there was no personal friendship between the two men. Connors had refused to join the Association of Tennis Professionals, the organization Ashe had helped start years earlier. Nor did Connors want any part of Davis Cup action, preferring to spend his time and talents at more lucrative tennis tournaments. When Ashe suggested that Connors's attitude toward Davis Cup play was "seemingly unpatriotic," Connors charged Ashe with libel and lobbed a $3 million lawsuit over the net. No, there was no love lost between these two men.

But as Arthur entered center court that July 5, 1975, he felt sure he could win. He knew, though, that he had to stay cool and cautious. Connors was a human hummingbird, the master of back-and-forth shots, often ending with a quick, well-placed blast. Ashe decided to play a slow, conservative game, trying to draw Connors into making his own mistakes. Youth is often impatient, and Connors was known to start slugging the ball if the game seemed to be dragging. Service was an important factor, too. Arthur decided to angle his serve in, then rush the net for a good volley into an unprotected spot. As to Connors's serve, he would chip a return to pull Connors in, then try for a lob over his opponent's head.

The game strategy worked beautifully, at least for the first two sets. In less than an hour, Ashe put Connors at a 6-1, 6-1 disadvantage. People in the crowd exchanged bewildered looks. Was this the championship men's singles match at Wimbledon? It hardly seemed so.

In the third set, Connors found his second wind. He scrambled back and managed to pull the set away from Ashe, 7-5. The crowd roared its approval, although the fans were clearly on Ashe's side. Reserved British spectators had little respect for the loud complaints and obscene gestures for which Connors had become famous. But people had come to see quality tennis, and they did not want to witness a massacre.

In the fourth set, Connors got off to a fast 3-0

lead, even breaking Ashe's serve. Worried that his game plan was crumbling, Arthur sat holding his head between games. He wondered if he should change his strategy. Maybe he should cut loose more.

No, Arthur decided. A defensive style was the best way to deal with the headstrong Connors. Returning to the contest, Ashe continued with his slow, unyielding battle.

The decision paid off. Connors grew frustrated at the steady, methodical tempo of play. He made foolish errors, missed easy shots, and hit into Ashe's best forehand and backhand shots. Connors's lead in the fourth set disappeared, and Ashe pulled out a surprising 6-4 win to capture the 1975 Wimbledon championship. The crowd rose to its feet, cheering and applauding. Around the world, reporters carried the news. "History was made today at Wimbledon, when the first black to ever play for the men's singles crown captured the top prize."

Arthur relished the moment. Of all his victories, this was the greatest. Indeed, he had come a long way from Brook Field Park.

Winning Wimbledon, as well as nine other tournaments, in 1975 shot Ashe back up the rankings ladder. In the past several years, others had

▲*Returning a powerful backhand to Jimmy Connors, Arthur battles for the title at Wimbledon in 1975.*

A triumphant Arthur Ashe raises the Wimbledon trophy.▶

pushed him out of the top ratings in the United States. Now he zoomed to the top—number one— not only in the nation but in the world. "It was a wonderful feeling," Ashe recalled, "yet when you're on top, the only direction you have to go is down. I knew there were plenty of players who were out to knock me off."

Whatever the case, Arthur enjoyed his moment of glory. He gave interviews and speeches, reaching out with motivational messages to black youth. "Some folks call tennis a rich people's sport or a white person's game," Ashe observed. "I guess I started too early, because I just thought it was something fun to do. Later, I discovered there was a lot of work to being good in tennis. You've got to make a lot of sacrifices and spend a lot of time if you really want to achieve with this sport, or in any sport, or in anything truly worthwhile. Is it worth the price? Well, I'm here to tell you it is. I'm also here to tell you that there's a lot more to be done— and there's a spot for you to do it. All you have to do is find it."

Whenever he turned around, a photographer was waiting to snap Arthur's picture. Most of the media people disappeared quickly after completing their assigned tasks. But Jeanne Marie Moutoussamy was different. A professional photographer, she showed up to take a few pictures after the United Negro College Fund tournament. Jeanne's quick conversation, peppered with witty humor, caught Arthur's attention. He also found it difficult not to notice her warm smile, long, dark hair, and slender figure. Yes, this woman radiated class and style. Before long, Arthur was taking her out, whenever he could. Unfortunately, he was away so often playing tournaments that their romance existed mostly over telephone wires.

While his feelings for Jeanne Moutoussamy increased, so did the problems stemming from his heel injury. Tournament wins dwindled in 1976, and he failed to repeat his Wimbledon victory. Another American, Vitas Gerulaitis, bumped him out in the fourth round. By early 1977, Arthur

Arthur and Jeanne exchange wedding vows.

made two major resolutions—he was going to have heel surgery and he was going to get married.

Arthur put creativity to work in his proposal. After buying an engagement ring for Jeanne, he slipped it inside an envelope and put it in her medicine cabinet in her bathroom. It took three days before Jeanne found the ring, but when she did, her answer came fast: "Yes!"

On February 20, 1977, Arthur Ashe stood in New York City's United Nations Chapel, a cast on his left leg. He watched his bride-to-be, Jeanne Marie Moutoussamy, come to his side. A new chapter in his life was beginning, and Arthur couldn't have been happier.

Chapter / Nine

Downhill Slide

Injuries continued to bother Arthur during 1977. They prevented him from entering both the Wimbledon competition and the U.S. Open. His rankings dropped, as did the number of manufacturers who had looked to Arthur to endorse their products. But Ashe had no intention of growing depressed. "Certainly, times had been better," he reflected later on, "but one lives in hope of finding new avenues to explore, different ways of living."

One way for Arthur came in the form of writing. He signed on to write articles for *Tennis* magazine, offering pointers, and he made television promotionals for the National Guard.

Not that Arthur was about to hang up his racket. Although he played with pain and strain at times, he continued to enter tournaments. He won a few, gaining enough confidence to earn a berth in the Grand Prix Masters at New York's Madison Square Garden in 1979. This tournament features the top eight tennis players in the world. Now, at age thirty-five, Arthur battled his way into the final match before falling to nineteen-year-old John McEnroe. "Age is sometimes difficult to accept," commented Ashe. "As I watched McEnroe's quick, poised moves, his speed and agility, I realized I was becoming an old man on the courts."

In the late night hours of Monday, July 30, 1979, Arthur awakened with a pain in his chest. At first, he brushed it off. Maybe he had eaten something that did not agree with him. But the pain persisted. By breakfast time, he felt better. He helped run two tennis clinics that day and was signing some autographs when the pain hit him again. It felt as if someone had dropped a piano on his chest. Cold sweat covered his body, and chills made him tremble. A doctor insisted that he head to the hospital. Reluctantly, Arthur agreed. The tennis player started a moment when he overheard the physician mention "heart attack" to the people in the admitting room.

But that's just what it was. It was no light warning tap, either. Arthur's case called for major repair. His doctors told him that unless he agreed to open-heart surgery, not only would he be unable to play tennis again but his life expectancy would be shortened. "Let's do it," Ashe replied.

In December, Arthur checked into St. Luke's Hospital in New York City. Carefully the physicians removed four veins from Arthur's leg and joined them to the obstructed arteries leading from the heart. Blood began to flow smoothly, and the operations were termed successful. One week later, Arthur confidently predicted he'd be playing in the 1980 Wimbledon matches.

It was not to be. Although Arthur continued to recover, any attempt at physical activity brought new pain and suffering. On April 16, 1980, a weary Arthur Ashe assembled media people for a news conference. "One must face the facts," he said. "The spirit is willing but the body says no. My days of tennis competition are over. I plan to begin a new season of writing, talking, listening, and assisting."

Actually, Arthur had already spent years pursuing those interests. Two autobiographies, *Advantage Ashe* and *Arthur Ashe: Portrait in Motion*, had won critical acclaim and popular attention among sports enthusiasts. His articles for *Tennis* magazine captured immediate attention, too. For years, Ashe had been in front of a microphone, speaking out on

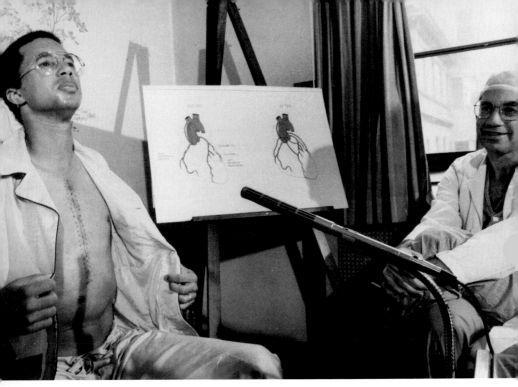

Arthur shows off his scar after undergoing bypass heart surgery.

topics ranging from apartheid to sports activities for the young. Polls among black youths found Ashe one of the most admired of their race. As a listener, Arthur had few equals. He opened his doors and his mind to people who shared ideas for improving all phases of tennis, especially players' rights. Civil rights leaders sought his counsel, too, hoping to win his endorsement for their causes. He was always willing to help out at tennis clinics for young and old, sharing constructive criticism and hints. Maybe Arthur Ashe would no longer dominate tennis courts, but he would continue to contribute to society.

The officials of the U.S. Davis Cup team were not about to let Arthur drop his active role in tennis. For ten years—1963, from 1965 to 1970, and in 1975, 1977, and 1978—Arthur had been a member of that distinguished squad. No one had given more with such dedication. Now, in 1981, those in charge asked Ashe to captain the team. Although he could not play as he had before, he could still bring out the best in other players. A grateful and modest Ashe accepted.

With the addition of court spitfire John McEnroe to the squad, Arthur faced an immediate challenge. No one questioned McEnroe's tennis talents—many players could not even return the southpaw's powerball serve—but his loud, obnoxious manners during tournament play ran in direct opposition to Ashe's refined, gentlemanly demeanor. The captain insisted on "the highest standards of sportsmanship," while McEnroe displayed some of the lowest. At one point in 1981, Ashe felt compelled to apologize for McEnroe and his "disgraceful" behavior. McEnroe volleyed back, claiming that a captain's job was to pump his players up rather than to tear them down. Despite the arguments, the U.S. Davis Cup team won the international championships in both 1981 and 1982.

In his spare time, and with the help of writing

aide Neil Amdur, Arthur produced a third autobiographical account of his life, *Off the Court*. Unfortunately, in 1983, Arthur faced health problems again. He had to undergo additional heart surgery, this time a double bypass operation.

"Although I know my good tennis days are behind me," Ashe told an audience of black youths in 1983, "I still think I am making a contribution to the game. When you love something as much as I love this sport, you can't just walk away from it. It has given me so much. I'd like to think I can still give something back."

In 1984, Jimmy Connors joined the Davis Cup team. Between McEnroe and Connors, the United States could boast a superpower duo. But their on-court behavior seldom matched their superb level of play. They took their anger and frustration out on referees, umpires, and even the fans, hurling foul language and making crude gestures. "They're two young brats who should be taken behind the woodshed," one veteran sportscaster observed. "Unfortunately, Arthur Ashe is not the one to do that. He is a first-class gentleman who would never understand their behavior and be able to deal with it."

That just about summed up the situation. After countless disagreements and noticeable strain among all parties involved, Ashe gave up his duties as Davis Cup captain in 1985. National television networks quickly put him under contract as a commentator for major tennis events.

Ever since 1969, when he was first refused a visa to travel to South Africa to play tennis, Arthur had spoken out against apartheid. "To sit back and know that racial segregation still thrives there is unconscionable. More must be done to bring about change." During January 1985, Ashe joined in an antiapartheid protest at the South African Embassy in Washington, D.C. It was the first time Ashe was arrested, but he went smiling off to jail, saying, "It is the least we can do in the name of freedom."

In March of that year, Arthur headed to Newport, Rhode Island, for induction into the Tennis Hall of Fame. He was cited for a career that started when he was only twelve, a boy in Richmond winning his first amateur competition. In all, his record stood at 818 wins and 260 losses, with a total of 51 tournament titles of the 304 open contests entered.

But as people listened to the induction speeches, many of them shared a thought. It was not the numbers that were important, as impressive as they were. It was *how* they had been obtained. "Sure, there have been better players than Ashe," noted

Under arrest! The renowned tennis star is handcuffed and led off to prison after demonstrating against apartheid at the South African Embassy in Washington, D.C.

one sportswriter, "but no one played with more class."

Although Arthur continued to be involved in tennis by working with both international and national organizations, his visits to the court were few and only recreational. The doctors wanted no further heart problems. Arthur accepted the role of campaign chairman of the American Heart Association, giving speeches and helping to acquaint the public with the causes of heart disease. He became the spokesperson for the Volvo-

Collegiate Series, too, a program promoting the goals of the country's thirty thousand intercollegiate tennis players.

But 1987 was not all business for Arthur Ashe. The arrival of a baby girl brought a special joy, "a miracle moment," as he called it later. Jeanne and Arthur named their new child Camera. Since the couple had met when Jeanne came to take Arthur's picture, the name seemed fitting.

Another trip to the hospital took place in September the following year. Arthur had been troubled by a numbness in his right hand. Doctors diagnosed a severe bacterial infection in his head that caused extreme nerve pressure. Brain surgery and antibiotics were prescribed.

But his condition was far more serious than it had first appeared. One day Arthur's team of physicians at New York Hospital shared the news. Blood- and tissue-testing during Arthur's stay had turned up tragic results. He was HIV positive. His blood contained the AIDS virus.

But how? Since when? He had never been sexually promiscuous or irresponsible. Intravenous drugs were never a part of his life. How else could he have contracted the virus?

Carefully and slowly, Arthur and his doctors examined all the possibilities. Everything seemed to point to his heart surgery back in 1983. He had received two pints of blood to hasten his recovery. That was some twenty-two months before all blood was automatically tested for HIV. Apparently that blood was infected.

Arthur and Jeanne agonized over the situation. Should he go public and share the news? Or should they keep it a secret? Jeanne leaned toward letting the public know. But Arthur was not so sure. There was Camera to think about. How could a little child handle the news? No, it would remain a secret, Arthur decided. Jeanne Ashe went along with his decision. After all, it was his life.

The year 1988 also saw publication of a scholarly three-volume set of books called *A Hard Road to Glory*. Carefully researched and "written with the heart as well as the mind," as Arthur described the 1,600-page project, the story of African Americans in sports proved both a critical and commercial success. Television rights were quickly snapped up.

In 1989, Arthur Ashe, Sr., died. His death removed the most enduring pillar of support in his son's life. "He was always there for me," the younger Ashe remembered. "I'd like to think I gave him some moments to be proud and happy." There seemed little doubt of that.

Arthur continued to refuse to be daunted by his health problems. He found a new cause to champion in Proposition 42 of the National Collegiate Athletic Association. The ruling prohibited athletic scholarships for incoming freshmen who did not have a 2.0 high school grade-point average and a minimum combined point score of 700 on the Scholastic Aptitude Test or a similar score on another academic test. Some black leaders and college coaches protested the ruling, claiming that it penalized minority groups. Appearing at a Black History Month gathering at Wichita State in February 1990, Ashe defended Proposition 42. He backed up his feelings with statistics, saying that although blacks made up only 6.5 percent of the student body populations at 290 NCAA Division 1 schools, blacks made up 58 percent of the basketball teams and 38 percent of the football teams. Sadly, only one out of five black athletes at those schools would ever graduate. "You don't really care about us as students," Ashe insisted. "You care about us as athletes, to fill your stadiums and arenas."

In November, Ashe spoke out about blacks in the tennis world. African Americans were tolerated in the sport, he asserted, because they were few in number. In *Tennis* magazine Ashe wrote that "the tennis community, and white society in general, is afraid that if we get our foot in the door, we'd do in tennis what we've done in basketball—take over."

In November 1991, Ashe eagerly accepted an invitation to visit South Africa with thirty-one other black leaders to evaluate the political changes. He was happy to note improved conditions for black South Africans, yet observed that "more remains to be done."

Although he maintained a busy schedule, Arthur felt some of his strength slipping. He tired quickly. Medication and treatment helped keep him going, but every now and then he felt too tired to move.

And then came the visit from the past. In April 1992, Doug Smith of *USA Today* confronted Arthur with questions about the dark secret kept for almost four years. Ashe felt trapped. There seemed to be no choice but to tell the world the whole story.

Chapter / Ten

Set Point

From the moment he finished his press conference on April 8, 1992, Arthur whirled into action. Whatever he did, he did with the thought of protecting little Camera. Surprisingly, the five-year-old girl seemed to understand more than he thought she would. She talked to her father openly about his illness. "Daddy, tell me how you got AIDS," the girl would say. "Do you feel sick today?" Carefully and slowly, her father would answer. He spent every moment he could with his daughter.

For both Camera and Jeanne, Arthur tried to maintain a strong front. As to the misfortune of contracting AIDS and his eventual death from the disease, Arthur shrugged. "I never ask 'Why me?' about my troubles. I would have to ask 'Why me?' about my blessings, too. Why my win-

Jeanne and Arthur with five-year-old Camera

ning Wimbledon? And why my marrying a beautiful, gifted woman and having a wonderful child?"

With the dark secret revealed, Arthur now had another cause. He became an advocate for AIDS education, willing to take the speaker's stand at meetings and gatherings. As people listened, there was a special sympathy for the man who was talking. This was a victim, a tragic, innocent victim of a horrible disease. He had not practiced unsafe sex or taken intravenous drugs. He had done nothing to bring about his condition other than have a blood transfusion. It could happen to anyone.

It was that awareness that made Arthur's message so personal and meaningful. In speaking one-to-one, his eyes behind the dark spectacles often said more than his words. It was all such a waste, so unfair.

Conscious that time could be running out, Arthur put his life into fast forward. He seemed to be thinking that the busier he was, the less he would have to think about the future—that future that contained so many question marks.

In June 1992, Ashe contacted author Arnold Rampersad, a professor of literature at Princeton, about writing a book, a personal memoir. The two men began work immediately.

When tennis luminaries assembled for the U.S. Open in September, Arthur announced a $5 million fund drive to combat AIDS. The kickoff followed on the heels of Arthur Ashe Day in New York City, proclaimed by the mayor and longtime friend David N. Dinkins.

A few days later, Ashe was again arrested in Washington, D.C., with eighty other protesters. This time he was opposing President George Bush's policy of returning Haitian refugees to their homeland. "Someone seems to have forgotten what the Statue of Liberty says to people coming here," commented Ashe. The day after his arrest, Arthur suffered another heart attack—a mild seizure, but frightening nonetheless. He was simply watching television at home. "Slow down!" seemed to be the warning.

For the sake of Camera and Jeanne, Arthur *did* try to slow his pace a bit. Yet by December 1, he sat before a meeting of United Nations delegates as part of World AIDS Day, sharing his thoughts. "We want to be able to look back and say to all concerned that we did what we had to do, when we had to do it, and with all the resources required," he told the delegates.

By the end of the year, Arthur looked with pride on new inner-city tennis programs for youth in Newark, New Jersey; Detroit; Kansas City, Missouri; Atlanta; and Indianapolis. Working with local officials in each area, Ashe shared his ideas and advice on opening new facilities and activities.

Within a month, as the new year began, Arthur's condition worsened. Medication and treatment did little to control the pain. Pneumonia forced Ashe into the hospital. Despite his ordeal, he directed his attention toward planning a Valentine's Day party for Camera and her friends.

The party was never held.

At 3:13 P.M., Saturday, February 6, 1993, Arthur Robert Ashe, Jr., died at New York Hospi-

Arthur marches outside the White House in support of Haitian refugees, and is arrested again.

tal. Pneumonia, a complication of AIDS, was given as the cause of death.

News of Ashe's death shocked the world. Everyone knew his health was precarious, but the unexpected announcement left many people stunned.

In Madison Square Garden, a raucous crowd attending the Riddick Bowe-Michael Dokes boxing match paused in silence as a bell tolled solemnly. On a tennis court in Japan, tennis star Martina Navratilova requested a moment of silence "to remember an extraordinary human being who transcended his sport, his race, religion and nationality and in his own way helped to change the world." From the White House, recently inaugurated President Bill Clinton noted that "Arthur Ashe never rested with fame. He used the strength of his voice and the power of his example to open the doors of opportunity for other African Americans, fighting discrimination in America and around the world. In the last years of his life he continued his tenacious battle for others in the face of a disease he could not beat. He was a true American hero and a great example to us all."

And on an empty tennis court in Richmond, Virginia, a young black boy silently slipped a handful of dandelions between the white strips of tennis netting. He straightened them in the single square and stepped back. His head bowed, the boy quietly walked away.

It was the tribute Arthur might have liked best.

Jeanne and Camera, surrounded by a sea of mourners, at Arthur's funeral.

Milestones in the Life of Arthur Robert Ashe, Jr.

1943 Born July 10 in Richmond, Virginia

1947 Moves to Brook Field Park in Richmond

1949 Begins playing tennis

1950 Mattie Ashe (mother) dies

1953 Begins training with Dr. Robert Walter Johnson

1955 Wins ATA twelve-and-under singles tournament/doubles tournament (with Willis Thomas)
Arthur Ashe, Sr. (father), remarries

1956 Wins ATA fifteen-and-under doubles tournament (with Willis Thomas)

1957 Wins ATA fifteen-and-under singles tournament

1958 Wins ATA fifteen-and-under singles tournament/doubles tournament (with Willis Thomas)

1960 Wins ATA eighteen-and-under singles tournament / ATA men's singles tournament / USLTA Junior Indoor singles tournament
Moves to St. Louis for senior year of high school

1961 Graduates, with highest grades in his class, from high school; earns athletic scholarship to University of California at Los Angeles
Wins ATA men's singles tournament / ATA men's doubles tournament (with Ronald Charity) / USLTA Junior Indoor singles tournament / U.S. Interscholastic singles tournament

1962 Wins ATA men's singles tournament

1963 Competes at Wimbledon for the first time
Becomes first black named to the U.S. Davis Cup team
Wins ATA men's singles tournament / U.S. Hardcourt tournament

1964 Wins Eastern Grass Court tournament

Receives Johnston Award for tennis sportsmanship / ability

1965 Wins NCAA singles tournament / NCAA doubles tournament (with Ian Crookenden)

1966 Honored at Arthur Ashe Day ceremonies in Richmond

Graduates from UCLA with B.S. degree in business administration

Inducted into the U.S. Army

Becomes assistant tennis coach at U.S. Military Academy

1967 Wins U.S. Clay Court singles tournament

Advantage Ashe is published

1968 Wins U.S. Nationals singles tournament and U.S. Open men's singles tournament

As part of the U.S. team, wins first of seven Davis Cup championships

1969 Works to establish International Tennis Players Association

Begins antiapartheid campaign against South Africa

1970 Wins U.S. Indoor doubles tournament (with Stan Smith)

Wins Australian Open singles tournament

1971 Wins French Open doubles tournament (with Marty Riessen)

1973 Competes in South African tournament, the first black to do so

1974 Serves as president of the Association of Tennis Professionals

1975 Wins World Championship Tennis singles tournament
Wins Wimbledon men's singles tournament
Arthur Ashe: Portrait in Motion is published

1977 Marries Jeanne Marie Moutoussamy on February 20 in New York City
Wins Australian Open doubles tournament (with Tony Roche)

1979 Suffers a heart attack and undergoes quadruple bypass surgery

1980 Retires from professional tennis competition

1981 Becomes captain of the U.S. Davis Cup team
Off the Court is published

1983 Undergoes double bypass surgery

1985 Inducted into the Tennis Hall of Fame
Resigns as Davis Cup team captain

1987 Daughter Camera Elizabeth is born

1988 *A Hard Road to Glory* is published
Learns he is HIV positive

1989 Announces support for NCAA academic requirements
Arthur Ashe, Sr. (father), dies

1991 Visits South Africa to observe political changes

1992 Publicly announces that he has contracted the AIDS virus

1993 Dies February 6 in New York City
Days of Grace: A Memoir is published

Abbreviations
Used in the Text

ATA   American Tennis Association
ATP   Association of Tennis Professionals
ITF   International Tennis Federation
ITPA   International Tennis Players Association
NCAA National Collegiate Athletic Association
ROTC Reserve Officers' Training Corps
USLTA United States Lawn Tennis Association
UCLA University of California at Los Angeles
WCT   World Championship Tennis

Selected Bibliography

Ashe, Arthur. *A Hard Road to Glory: A History of the African-American Athlete*. 3 volumes. New York: Warner Books, 1988.

Ashe, Arthur. *Arthur Ashe's Tennis Clinic*. Norwalk, CT: Golf Digest/Tennis, 1981.

Ashe, Arthur, with Neil Amdur. *Off the Court*. New York: New American Library, 1981.

Ashe, Arthur, with Frank Deford. *Arthur Ashe: Portrait in Motion*. Boston: Houghton Mifflin, 1975.

Ashe, Arthur, and Clifford Gewecke, Jr. *Advantage Ashe*. New York: Coward-McCann, 1967.

Ashe, Arthur, and Arnold Rampersad. *Days of Grace: A Memoir*. New York: Knopf, 1993.

Little, Alan. *Wimbledon Men: A Hundred Championships. 1877-1986*. London: Wimbledon Lawn Tennis Association, 1986.

Lorge, Barry. "Lessons in Living." *Tennis* magazine, April 1993.

Robinson, Louie, Jr. *Arthur Ashe, Tennis Champion*. Garden City, NY: Doubleday, 1967.

Weissberg, Ted. *Arthur Ashe: Tennis Great*. New York: Chelsea House, 1991.

/Index

95162

921
Ash